The
Nautical
Institute

Navigation assessments –
a guide to best practice

by
Harry Gale FNI

Navigation assessments – a guide to best practice

Published by The Nautical Institute
202 Lambeth Road, London SE1 7LQ, England
Tel: +44 (0)20 7928 1351   Fax: +44 (0)20 7401 2817   Web: www.nautinst.org
© The Nautical Institute 2016

ISBN 978 1 906915 51 3

This book has been prepared to address the subject of navigation assessments. This should not, however, be taken to mean that this document deals comprehensively with all of the concerns that will need to be addressed or even, where a particular matter is addressed, that this document sets out the only definitive view for all situations. The opinions expressed are those of the author only and are not necessarily to be taken as the policies or views of any organisation with which they have any connection.

Readers of *Navigation assessments – a practical guide* are advised to make themselves aware of any applicable local, national or international legislation or administrative requirements or advice which may affect decisions taken onboard.

Cover image Danny Cornelissen
Publisher Bridget Hogan
Book editor Stephen Spark
Typesetting and layout by Phil McAllister Design
Printed in UK by Cambrian Printers, Aberystwyth

Foreword

Steve Clinch
Chief Inspector of Marine Accidents
UK Marine Accidents Investigation Branch

I was very pleased to be asked to write this foreword to the Nautical Institute's latest guide to best practice.

I became a fan of "navigational and safety audits" (the term used by the company I worked for) more than 20 years ago when I was involved in the management of a fleet of Capesize bulk carriers. In those days the audits were primarily designed to give the shore-based management team confidence that the company's procedures were being followed.

It was recognised that conducting audits in port was impracticable because of the limited time available and the pressures such audits placed on ship's staff at a time when they were most busy. So it was the custom for the audit team to board our vessels when they were passing Las Palmas *en route* to North West European discharging ports. This allowed around four days of sea passage time for the auditors to assess the performance of the ship's staff under 'normal' conditions. Nonetheless such audits were stressful experiences for the ship's company and, looking back, I'm not sure they always managed to obtain a true picture of how the ship was operating.

The causes and circumstances of marine accidents almost always include systemic problems. In my current job, I see many examples where there is a clear disconnect between the navigational standards and procedures contained in company safety management systems and what really happens on board ships that have been involved in an accident.

Today, the challenge for any ship manager is the same as it was 20 years ago to know whether his/her fleet is operating in accordance with the procedures and guidelines provided to each vessel. Do ship's staff really buy into the company's

Foreword

Navigation assessments – a guide to best practice

safety management system? Do they share a common safety culture? Of particular concern will be whether bridge teams are adhering to best practice to minimise the ever-present risks of collision and groundings. These are questions that are difficult to answer from an office chair ashore or a superintendent's flying visit in port.

This book provides a detailed guide to answering these questions through the application of at-sea navigational assessments. Note the term "assessment" rather than "audit". The methodology described in the guide is thorough but practical, and is designed to be more inclusive (and less stressful) for ships' bridge teams than traditional audits. While the ultimate purpose of an at-sea navigational assessment is to identify weaknesses or gaps in shipboard procedures, the coaching, consultation and feedback between the assessor and bridge team will help break down barriers and build stronger safety cultures. Examples of the findings of marine accident investigations from around the world also add compelling context to the importance of adhering to best practice when navigating vessels at sea.

In my view, every ship's manager, Master, deck officer and navigational assessor should have a copy of this guide to hand, no matter what their experience.

Acknowledgements

This book seeks to help all those engaged in navigation assessments, whether conducting them or undergoing them. The Nautical Institute would like to thank all who were involved in contributing to this endeavour, especially peer reviewers and all those who gave advice and support.

Special thanks are due to the following:

Capt Sarabjit Butalia FNI – Seagoing Master
Capt Mark Bull FNI – Marine Consultant
Capt Yves Vandenborn AFNI – The Standard Club
Clive Rees – The Standard Club
Capt Yusuf Soomro FNI – TMC Marine
Tony Wynne – Technical Adviser, OCIMF
The NI SeaGoing Correspondence Group
The NI LinkedIn Group

Contents

Contents
Navigation assessments – a guide to best practice

Case studies

There are multiple lessons to be learned from the case studies in this book and you will see multiple references to the same casualties in the text. The case studies only give an outline of the casualty and we hope that you will be motivated to look at a more comprehensive account in the accident investigation report. Links to these can be found in this reference list.

Arslan II grounding on Arklow Bank, 14 January 2014
MCIB Ireland Report MCIB/235 no 6 of 2014 www.mcib.ie
Section 3 page 36

Atlantic Blue grounding at Kirkcaldie Reef, Torres Strait, 7 February 2009
Australian Transport Safety Bureau Marine Occurrence Investigation no 262 MO-2009-001 www.atsb.gov.au
Section 3 page 47

Bonden/Asian Breeze collision in the fairway off Malmö, 16 March 2015
Swedish Accident Investigation Authority (SHK) Report RS 2016:01e www.havkom.se
Section 3 page 48

Bow Mariner explosion off the coast of Virginia on 28 February 2004
US Coast Guard Marine Safety Office Report www.uscg.mil
Section 5 page 70

Bunga Teratai Satu grounding on the Great Barrier Reef, 2 November 2000
ATSB Marine Safety Investigation Report 162 www.atsb.gov.au
Section 5 page 70

Capri/Brightoil Legend allision in the Eastern Special Purpose 'A' Anchorage, Singapore, 9 July 2015
Transport Malta Marine Safety Investigation Report no 12/2016 mti.gov.mt
Section 3 page 44

CMA CGM Florida/Chou Shan collision in East China Sea, 19 March 2013
UK MAIB Report no 11/2014 assets.publishing.service.gov.uk
Sections 3, 5 pages 41, 66, 70

Conti Peridot/Carla Mærsk collision in Houston Ship Channel, 9 March 2015
NTSB/MAR 16/01 PB2016-103277 www.ntsb.gov
Section 5 page 69

Costa Concordia grounding on Giglio, 13 January 2012
Italian Ministry of Infrastructures and Transports Marine Casualties Investigative
Body http://3kbo302xo3lg2i1rj8450xje.wpengine.netdna-cdn.com/wp-content/
uploads/2013/05/Costa_Concordia_-_Full_Investigation_Report.pdf
Section 5 page 65

Doric Chariot grounding at Piper Reef, North Queensland, 29 July 2002
ATSB Marine Safety Investigation Report 182 www.atsb.gov.au
Section 3 page 46

Ever Smart/Alexandra collision at Jebel Ali, 11 February 2015
UK MAIB Report no 28/2015 assets.publishing.service.gov.uk
Section 3 page 42

Hamburg grounding in the Sound of Mull, Scotland, 11 May 2015
UK MAIB Report no 12/2016 assets.publishing.service.gov.uk
Sections 3, 4 pages 32, 60

Hyundai Dominion/Sky Hope collision in East China Sea, 21 June 2004
UK MAIB Report no 17/2005 assets.publishing.service.gov.uk
Section 2 page 23

Katre/Statengracht collision in the Baltic Sea, 2 February 2013
Transport Malta Marine Safety Investigation Report no 04/2014 mti.gov.mt
Section 3 page 39

Lysblink Seaways grounding at Kilchoan, 18 February 2015
UK MAIB Report no 25/2015 assets.publishing.service.gov.uk
Section 4 page 63

Maersk Garonne **grounding Fremantle, Western Australia, 28 February 2015**
Marine Occurrence Investigation 319-MO-2015-002 www.atsb.gov.au
Section 3 page 45

Maersk Kendal **grounding on Monggok Sebarok reef in the Singapore Strait,
16 September 2009**
UK MAIB Report no 2/2010 assets.publishing.service.gov.uk
Section 4 page 61

Navigator Scorpio **grounding on Haisborough Sand, North Sea, 3 January 2014**
UK MAIB Report no 30/2014 assets.publishing.service.gov.uk
Section 2 page 27

Norwegian Dream/Ever Decent **collision in the approaches to the Dover Strait,
24 August 1999**
Bahamas Maritime Authority Report email for a copy: casualty@bahamasmaritime.com
Section 1 page 6

Oliva **grounding on Nightingale Island, Tristan Da Cunha, 16 March 2011**
Transport Malta Marine Safety Investigation Report no 14/2012
www.islandvulnerability.org
Section 2 page 24

Ostende Max/Formosaproduct Brick **collision in Malacca Strait, 18 August 2009**
Isle of Man Casualty Investigation Report no CA107 www.gov.im
Section 1 page 8

Overseas Reymar **allision with San Francisco–Oakland Bay Bridge, 7 January 2013**
NTSB Report DCA-13-LM-004 www.ntsb.gov
Section 3 page 45

Ovit **grounding in Dover Strait, 18 September 2013**
UK MAIB Report no 24/2014 assets.publishing.service.gov.uk
Section 1 page 11

Paula C/Darya Gayatri **collision in the Dover Strait Traffic Separation Scheme, 11 December 2013**
UK MAIB Report no 25/2014 assets.publishing.service.gov.uk
Section 3 page 37

Rena **grounding on Astrolabe Reef, 5 October 2011**
New Zealand Transport Accident Investigation Commission Final Report 11-204
December 2014 www.taic.org.nz
Sections 1, 3 pages 17, 43

Sp**ring Glory/Josephine Mærsk collision in the eastern approaches to the Singapore Strait, 5 June 2012**
Danish MAIB Report case no 2012005988 www.dmaib.com
Sections 3, 5 pages 40, 66

Sundstraum/Kapitan Lus **collision off Copenhagen, 3 July 2009**
Accident Investigation Board Norway Report Mar 2010/10 www.aibn.no
Section 3 page 38

Tongala/Bo Spring **collision off coast of Philippines, 7 May 2015**
Transport Malta Marine Safety Investigation Report no 07/2016 mti.gov.mt
Section 3 page 43

Vega Sagittarius **grounding off Greenland, 16 August 2012**
Danish MAIB Report case no 2012003009 www.dmaib.com
Section 3 page 51

Wes Janine/Stenberg **collision at anchorage off Brunsbüttel, 16 January 2014**
BSU Investigation Report 36/14 www.bsu-bund.de
Sections 3, 5 pages 53, 68

Section 1

Introduction

A ship spends up to 90% of its time at sea, so navigation and navigation incidents are considered to be the shipowner's largest risk. The competence of bridge watchkeeping officers is therefore of paramount importance to the shipowner.

Much depends on the training and skill levels attained by the bridge team. According to the Swedish Club, 50% of claims are attributed to navigation incidents, chiefly caused by lack of situational awareness, poor lookout and complacency.

Many external audit programmes exist, and navigation audits are needed for ISM audits and SIRE inspections, but they may not identify lapses in bridge procedures.

There are negative connotations associated with the word 'audit'. This is why we have chosen the word 'assessment' instead, in the hope that assessors will approach the task in a way that doesn't demotivate people and that maintains morale. This softer approach should also encourage crews to be truthful with assessors, confident that there will be no disciplinary action resulting from the process.

It is clear from accident reports, a number of which are used in this book, that best practice is not always being complied with and that lessons learned from bridge resource management (BRM) training are not being applied in the shipboard environment. Navigation assessments should be used to identify any lapses.

BRM is effective only if all participants – including managers – are encouraged to support the concept and to change their behaviour. This is possible only if the culture on the bridge is the same as that taught in BRM. That, though, is rarely the case. We examine the cultural issues relevant to this in Section 5.

Many Masters have never seen BRM performed properly, so are reluctant or unable to implement it on board, particularly if their company doesn't conduct effective navigation assessments. As a result, the effectiveness of some BRM programmes has been brought into question. If there is no perceptible change in behaviour when the officers return on board after training, then the company has squandered its investment in the programme.

Case study

Norwegian Dream/Ever Decent Dover Strait August 1999. The report recommended constant reviews of the risks posed by systems and practices on board and an examination of the ways in which those risks are being managed. It pointed out that, properly used, an ISM audit could provide a useful examination of ship operations, but it would not cover the practices of individuals and would not look at navigation systems.

Throughout this book case studies will be used to provide examples to help assessors demonstrate to ship's staff the consequences of the failure of navigation procedures. Case studies are useful for highlighting, as in Section 3, operational and system failures that resulted in collision or grounding. Many of the cases can be used to illustrate failure in more than one of the procedures, and assessors may have their own favourites. The Nautical Institute publication *Navigation Accidents and their Causes* includes many more case studies.

In addition, we have consulted widely on the issue of navigation assessments to try to obtain a clear picture of the practicalities faced. For instance, we have used elements of the discussion on this issue by members of The Nautical Institute's LinkedIn group, our Sea-Going Correspondents Group (SGCG) and in a survey of other maritime professionals.

NI LinkedIn group

❝ *Ships' navigation teams know what the procedures are, but trade off full compliance with getting that and 1,001 other tasks done because they will be judged on quantity and not quality. After a while this culture grows into something really risky – a perception that 'compliance' is for presentation purposes only. The way things are really done involves the acceptance of huge amounts of risk because it's become the norm.*

That attitude works its way back to the student at college, who believes that what is taught in the classroom is all part of the act, but what really goes on is what that student will return to: a trade-off of thoroughness for efficiency in order to get through the day. 〞

In June 2012 The Standard Club issued a safety bulletin, which concluded that there was "overriding evidence" that the frequency and cost of navigation incidents were increasing and warned that this was having an adverse effect on company reputations. The club was adamant that the major cause of navigation incidents was human error stemming from poor training. However, the club also reported that in a "significant number" of navigation incidents watchkeepers had received BRM training, which casts doubt on the effectiveness of that training. The club added that there was "strong evidence" that in many instances training was not being conducted well.

That is just one of many voices saying that reasonable standards of BRM are not being universally applied and that this leads directly to incidents. This cannot be allowed to continue.

So what is the solution? Increasingly it is recognised that a quality assessment of a ship's navigation is a valuable method to evaluate the effectiveness of BRM and reduce navigational risks.

Navigation incidents occur as a result of a failure to apply basic traditional navigation procedures such as maintaining a lookout, determining if a risk of collision with other vessels exists and taking appropriate action according to the Colregs.

The techniques for safe navigation are widely known and, when mastered and professionally carried out, reduce navigation risks. Why, then, is training not applied or procedures not followed? If there has been training, then the reasons for an accident may not be lack of knowledge, but rather the workload and pressure experienced by ships' officers.

What measures can be put in place to help officers apply their training and follow procedures? It is increasingly obvious from the case studies throughout this book that many headline-generating navigation incidents could have been prevented by effective navigation assessments. These should evaluate how the navigation of the ship is conducted and suggest proper corrective action that officers can put in place.

Case study

Ostende Max/Formosaproduct Brick, Malacca Strait, August 2009. This case illustrates the unfortunate consequences of failure to apply rules or procedures (see Swiss cheese diagram, page 13). The report concluded that serious failings in bridge team management (BTM), poor situational awareness, complacency, distraction and confusion by members of the bridge team led to inadequate assessment of the risk of collision and lack of appropriate action to avoid collision in compliance with the Colregs.

The report recommended a thorough review into the company's application of BTM and its effective implementation. The company was urged to conduct stricter auditing to ensure proper compliance with company procedures, application of Colregs, BTM and lookout practices and where possible for this audit to be conducted while on passage.

What is an assessment?

Most people will probably agree that assessments should be independent and systematic and should evaluate evidence objectively. However, it is the way the documentation is handled that causes concern.

If everything is done by checklist unease sets in, because checklists can be ineffective. The questions asked during such 'checklist inspections' tend to be leading, closed and authoritative, leaving limited opportunity for expression, discussion or debate. There is little benefit if, when an assessor identifies some non-conformities, the company merely produces more checklists and procedures. There is very little foresight and thinking in this mundane 'check-do' process. Sailing for just a few days, conducting an assessment and issuing notice of some non-conformities is not sufficient.

A more holistic approach is required to achieve the desired objective and to help the ship's Master and officers to feel professional about their navigation practices. When assessors identify gaps in procedures, they can discuss these with Masters and officers and together find ways to implement solutions. Policy or procedural non-conformities can be reported to the company for follow-up. It is much better to suggest improvements while on board so officers have the opportunity to discuss the procedures and objectives and get explanations for anything that is not understood. Assessors should not just make long lists of observations and leave the issues for Masters to deal with. Instead, they should sit down with Masters and discuss how any issues can be addressed by the team on the vessel and which ones should be referred to the office. It is at this stage that it should be made clear if there is a need for more training or if it is the case that any training the staff has received needs to be applied.

Many companies include navigation assessments as part of the routine ISM/SMS audits conducted by technical superintendents while ships are alongside in port. There is no value in this as a navigation assessment. Port inspections of passage plans, chart corrections or compass errors do not add up to a navigation assessment. Worse, this approach is likely to have a hugely negative impact on ship's staff, as this superficial intervention will disturb the ship's usual operations, staff rest hours and shore leave merely to briefly view checklists.

NI LinkedIn group

66 *Rather than call them audits, I would prefer to use the term navigation assessments. This reflects how they aim to gain an overall view of navigation standards measured against industry criteria and to assess how much they conform to company policies, standing orders and navigation procedures.* 99

In discussion with mariners at sea and others in the industry, we agree with the use of the term navigation assessments. The book will examine the process of conducting navigation assessments that are aimed at identifying gaps in how the ship is navigated and that suggest improvements.

All this is set against the background of calls for more stringent assessments and audits – but there is a need to decide what form these should take. As in all matters to do with ships, the more effective action is likely to be one that is uniform across the industry.

Discussions from our three sources showed that there are some conflicting ideas on navigation assessments and how they should be carried out. These range from systems that involve assessors sailing for several days on a vessel to those that only require a snapshot, usually in port, with a document trail to show company diligence. The snapshot approach doesn't show how navigation is actually conducted on the vessel, nor the potential gaps in training or effective working.

Navigation assessments – a guide to best practice

As part of its research on this topic, the Institute conducted a survey of more than 300 maritime professionals, with contributions from assessors (internal and external) on one side and Shipmasters and officers on the other.

Issues identified by assessors during navigation assessments included:

- Checklists completed without adequate checking
- Over-reliance on electronic navaids
- Lack of competence of the bridge team.

On the other hand, a large majority of the mariners in the survey thought positively of the assessments they had undergone. Many welcomed the fact that poor navigation practices or training needs were identified. Only 12% of seafarers questioned thought the assessment's aim was to find fault and place blame.

However, some officers questioned the need for navigation assessments on top of the other audits they are subjected to – including ISM, SMS and SIRE. They felt that navigation assessments only duplicated these, but ISM, SMS and SIRE do not concentrate on navigation to the degree that specialist navigation assessments do.

Responsible ship operators have carried out navigation assessments for many years and continue to do so using internal or external specialists. Many of these are tanker operators that want to meet the requirements for Tanker Management Self-Assessment (TMSA) inspections.

These operators know that however well trained and mentored watchkeepers may be, their practices and behaviour on board need to be monitored. Only by spending time on the vessel to assess the navigation practices can an assessor really get a feel for the watchkeepers' attitude.

If the company's own management carries out the assessment or delegates it to seagoing staff there may be dilution of the findings. This is particularly the case if the in-house QHSE team only visit the ship once a year to carry out all audits in one go – such as ISM, MLC, ISPS, navigation and environment. One of the benefits of engaging third-party assessors is that the findings are objective and will include feedback on the effectiveness and practicalities of procedures that ship's staff may be unwilling to comment on.

An assessment is an inspection based on sampling and it is therefore very important to know what to sample. In the NI survey, 83% of the assessors used a standard checklist; but if these checklists seek yes or no answers they won't help the assessor decide what to sample. A checklist with only yes or no answers should never form part of an assessment.

That is not to say that checklists are without value. They can be a useful aid for the assessor, ensuring activities are not forgotten or overlooked. The weakness is they can be used as a script that is rigorously followed without deviation. It is the uses that checklists are put to that matter. The vessel's SMS, if it addresses elements of navigation, can be used as an *aide memoire* to verify awareness, understanding and application and help save time in note-taking. However, it should be noted that STCW, the fifth edition of the ICS *Bridge Procedure Guide* (*BPG5*) and SIRE require robust procedures covering specific activities. The absence of these procedures would be a major non-conformity.

Case study

Ovit, Dover Strait, September 2013. An internal audit and SIRE inspection before the incident did not identify non-conformities in the navigation practices and procedures. The report noted serious errors in the conduct of the vessel's navigation, which a proper navigation assessment would have identified. This included shortcomings in the passage plan, lack of familiarity with ECDIS, poor situational awareness and monitoring of the passage. The passage was planned by an inexperienced and unsupervised junior officer and the plan was not checked by the Master before departure or by the OOW at the start of his watch. The ship's position was monitored solely against the intended track shown on the ECDIS, and navigation marks on the Varne Bank were seen but not acted upon. Although training in the use of the ECDIS fitted to the vessel had been provided, the Master and deck officers were unable to use the system effectively.

The report concluded that *Ovit's* SMS bridge procedures were comprehensive and included extensive guidance on the conduct of navigation using ECDIS. However, the serious shortcomings with the navigation had not been identified during the vessel's recent audits and inspections and the lack of BRM in the onboard management and associated navigation practices led to the grounding.

The case of the *Ovit* provides a perfect example of auditing by tickbox not being sufficient to show whether the vessel's procedures were really in compliance. One SGCG correspondent commented on the *Ovit* incident:

" *There was a blind assumption by the operator that its navigators were competent. There was a grossly unprofessional navigational culture on board at all levels, and poor application of an otherwise adequate quality system by the operator's managers. More effective navigation training, a focus on effective navigational audits by ship operators and port state control and more recourse to third-party navigational audits would provide solutions.* "

How far should an assessment go?

The depth to which a procedure is probed when carrying out the assessment depends on how important the activity is. It should be much more than ticking off boxes and the assessor needs to actually observe the officers and procedures. The aim is to identify knowledge gaps and to continually improve navigation practices, not to become engaged with petty issues. Assessors should use their knowledge of regulations and rules intelligently to identify risks specific to the navigation of the vessel. However, care should be taken by assessors to identify any small issues that have the potential to generate severe consequences.

So navigation assessments should:

- Determine the operational efficiency on the bridge
- Assess how the ship is navigated
- Identify important navigation and bridge management errors.

These errors in themselves may not cause an incident, but collectively could lead to a collision or grounding. The Swiss cheese accident trajectory model, developed by Professor James Reason, illustrates how errors need not become accidents.

Reason's Swiss cheese model. Cheese slices represent the barriers to accidents and the holes show the failures and weaknesses in navigation processes that could lead to one

The holes represent failures in the barriers and would be classed as 'non-conformities' in the navigation assessment. This illustrates clearly that if there are sufficient barriers in place, an accident will only occur when all of those barriers fail and the holes align. The key is to ensure that enough barriers are in place so that the failure of any one will not be disastrous. Barriers must be established at the operational level on board the ship and in the shipping company organisation. If the Master is able to complete the voyage without incident, the system has worked.

In the NI survey, 12% of the mariners said their company had no procedures for carrying out navigation assessments of the bridge team, while 32% said assessments are conducted only occasionally.

So how effective are assessments if the ship has prepared for them? Will bridge team members go back to their normal conduct when the assessor has departed? How does the assessor evaluate whether the conduct of navigation during the assessment period is the norm? The areas that require attention should be obvious to a good assessor, as the bridge team will revert to their normal watchkeeping practices after a few hours. This is the value of staying on board for several days.

NI LinkedIn group

66 *My experience of audits, navigational or otherwise, is that the crew and officers soon learn the answers and know what to expect. The whole exercise begins with wariness toward the process. Although the intention is not to promote a blame culture,*

Section 1
Navigation assessments – a guide to best practice

it is certainly viewed in that way by the shipboard staff. After all, if the OOW provides an unsatisfactory explanation to a query by the auditor, his competency is in question. It becomes a one-way communication rather than an exchange of ideas to identify the problem and look for a solution. 🗩

In preparation for assessment, 30% of the assessors in the NI survey said members of the ship's staff were well prepared and aware of the procedures for assessment with 60% saying there was some preparation before the assessment.

Assessments should preferably be undertaken on short coastal voyages where all aspects of the navigation of the vessel can be assessed, including pilotage. They should be of sufficient length to allow for assessment of navigation practices and the performance of the bridge team. The Nautical Institute is of the opinion that five days on board is the ideal time as this allows full observation of the OOWs, gives time for several group training and discussion sessions, and enables both night-time and daytime observations.

However, few navigation assessments meet this standard. In the survey by The Nautical Institute, 50% of the assessors took two to three days; 43% less than one day. This compares with the experience of shipboard personnel, 35% of whom experienced assessments of two to three days and 50% less than one day.

A five-day assessment, carried out while the vessel is at sea, allows proper judgement to be made on the success of bridge team management and what improvements are needed. It gives time to study the bridge team's familiarity with:

- Bridge equipment
- Communication equipment
- Distress procedures
- Navigation procedures
- Emergency plans
- Contingency plans
- Company forms amd documentation
- Company checklists.

The assessor should look at the time allotted to full familiarisation of the modern bridge. Are newly joined officers left on their own once the ship sails or is there a system to support them?

In practice, this means that over the course of an assessment, OOWs must show that they can confidently operate every piece of equipment. They must know the bridge and the control console thoroughly, particularly the menus and various buttons on the controls of the ECDIS and radar equipment.

One consequence of conducting an assessment during a short voyage is that it is likely to make the bridge team apprehensive. Assessors should therefore do their best to ensure that their presence on the bridge does not affect the bridge team's performance. The assessment should be carried out with minimum disruption and the assessor needs to be flexible and adapt to the ship's routine. Obviously all ships' staff will make an effort to improve their performance when undergoing assessment – this is only natural and to be expected, but they cannot maintain this for long. At some stage during their watch they will revert to type. Areas that require attention will soon become obvious to a good assessor.

One respondent in the NI survey said: "The junior officers were clearly intimidated by my presence and took some time to relax into their normal practices, whereas the seniors appeared consistent in their watchkeeping practices."

When performance is considered to be below the expected level, the issue should be discussed in a non-judgemental, open and fair manner. Assessors should be aware of any bias, 'spin', interpretations or assumptions that they may make.

Assessors face challenges due to the complex patterns of employment in shipping. The multicultural environment on board can create unusual dynamics in crew relationships. It is commonplace to have crews made up of three or four nationalities, and these cultures will vary in their approach to work, hierarchy and self-image.

These issues must be factored into any assessment and assessors need to be aware of the impact of culture and ethnicity. There are dangers of stereotyping and having ill-informed, preconceived assumptions and beliefs about different cultures. However, knowledge about the way people of different cultures may react in various situations is helpful and can form a basis for anticipating and preventing conflict and misunderstanding.

Section 1
Navigation assessments – a guide to best practice

Poor communication on board can occur as a result of:

- Lack of time: rushing and not providing full information
- Lack of competence: not having adequate skills
- Language barriers: not speaking a common language
- Physical barriers: trying to communicate in a noisy engine room or across a deck
- Hierarchy: not totally open with seniors or juniors
- Feelings and emotions: fear, apathy, frustration.

Regardless of the potential barriers, successful communication is more likely to occur when those involved are committed to being understood. As simple as this may sound, this is very often the first aspect of managing effective communication.

Assessors need to choose the right moment. This will be when the Master is not distracted or overburdened. Useful techniques include obtaining feedback, double-checking and reinforcing the message using multiple channels.

The importance of listening must not be overlooked. Distinguishing hearing from listening is vital, since the latter focuses not just on the message itself, but also includes the meaning and intention behind the message. What is hidden in the message, or even omitted, can sometimes be more revealing than the actual content.

Picking up non-verbal clues, understanding the context in which the communication is taking place and seeing the larger picture can help to improve communication. Observation of gestures, facial expressions, tone of voice and body posture will provide clues to the thoughts, feelings and intentions that very often are not communicated through words.

More information on multi-nationalism and communication is available in The Nautical Institute's publication *Human Performance and Limitation for Mariners*.

Although assessments have a very important role to play in providing opportunities for coaching and training, it is the Master's responsibility to ensure these are put into practice.

No one feels totally comfortable under assessment, but it is now normal practice in the industry and, when closely linked to training requirements, assessments work reasonably well. There needs to be management commitment to ensure there is enough time for a proper navigation assessment leading to education and guidance for the shipboard officers for them to be successful. At no point should this be seen as an exercise to catch out shipboard officers for any faults.

Case study

Rena, Astralobe Reef, October 2011. The report pointed out that a single assessment cannot realistically cover every aspect of a ship's operation, but recommended monitoring past and present performance to decide on which areas to concentrate. Six months before the grounding the *Rena*'s DPA sailed on the vessel for four days to conduct an internal ISM Code audit of its safety management system (SMS). The audit report listed several deficiencies, showing that the audit did cover bridge procedures to some degree. Given that crew members generally lift their performance immediately before and during a planned audit, it was difficult for the auditor to identify any non-conformities or observations that would otherwise be raised. While he was on board, the crew were not complying with the SMS with respect to passage planning, execution and position-fixing. However, the DPA's audit report did not note any other deficiencies regarding navigation or watchkeeping practices.

Some NI branches have convened technical meetings on various aspects of navigation assessments. A meeting of the US Gulf Branch discussed how assessments should be structured, conducted, audited and improved. Participants recognised that most companies wanted to see good results, but called for these appraisals to be viewed as assessments, not audits, in order to change perceptions. The meeting confirmed that assessments should verify that bridge procedures are actually being followed.

Disquiet was expressed that due to the constraints of budgets, time and commercial pressures, many companies request in-port navigation audits. Members considered these difficult, if not impossible, to undertake adequately. It was pointed out that in port there are too many other tasks under observation and that many of the tasks to be assessed in a navigation assessment are best viewed when underway. The branch found that many companies are reluctant to pay for the three- to five-day underway assessment that is needed if they are to gain a full understanding of what happens on the bridge.

Section 1
Navigation assessments – a guide to best practice

Branch discussions concluded that a thorough understanding of what is happening on the bridge can be gained only by observing full departure and arrival, from berth to berth. Several watch changes should be observed and assessors need to ensure the bridge team has full understanding of the various bridge watch conditions and the Master's standing orders.

Concern was expressed that crewing levels and fatigue continue to be a barrier to the effectiveness of navigation assessments. Other problems revolve around regulations for navigation in a safety fairway and staying in hand-steering.

However, it was acknowledged that navigation assessments are not designed to find fault but to assist with continuous improvement and should not list deficiencies alone. Assessments should set out what regulations or standards were not met, provide recommendations on how to meet them and ensure that solutions or best practices are shared with the Master first and then the crew. Should there be a problem then the conclusion of the assessment is the time to discuss it.

Section 2

Pre-assessment

Before an assessment begins, it is important to consider the attributes that a good assessor should possess. Assessors should be qualified Master Mariners with command experience who possess the knowledge and skills necessary to conduct the assessment; without this they will struggle to gain credibility on board. Navigation is a dynamic process and assessors should have sufficient competence and experience in the latest technology.

Assessors should be professional in their approach and be:

- Tactful
- Trained
- Prepared
- Patient
- Respectful.

Pre-assessment

Effective assessment will always be helped by preparation to ensure that the assessor shows professional knowledge and courtesy to the crew when they go on board. The assessor should not go on board without basic knowledge – for instance knowing the nationalities of the crew and whether the ship has ECDIS.

The assessor should be well versed in the company's implementation, expectations and practical application of navigation procedures in their fleet. Effective note-taking is an essential skill for any assessor. Memory is highly fallible and is no substitute for good notes. Voluminous notes are not necessary; recording key information only is good practice. A camera is a good assistant.

Section 2
Navigation assessments – a guide to best practice

Before going on board the assessor needs to decide how they will conduct the assessment. It is important always to be sensitive when talking to people, taking care not to be offensive or insulting, condescending or unfair; the assessor should be respectful of both individual officers and the environment in which they work. Effective assessments are conducted in a climate of co-operation rather than confrontation.

An assessor must be thoroughly prepared and be prepared to be patient. To fully understand the system in operation they may need to consider and explore matters from different angles.

A new approach may be required to achieve the desired objective of making the ship's Master and officers feel professional about their own navigation.

The professional onboard approach

The essentials for maintaining a professional approach on board are well trained and appropriately mentored officers, backed up by solid support from shore management for navigation skills. An assessor should take any opportunity to motivate members of the bridge team by identifying their own best practices.

The first step is to conduct a gap analysis combining interviews, a review of navigation processes and verification of its application or compliance. This should identify knowledge gaps and any deviation from standards and best practices. Interviews should be conducted at the end of watches or other activities to avoid distracting OOWs. If non-conformities are identified, the assessor should find out why they exist and tackle the root cause where possible. However, if bad procedures are identified an assessor cannot change them.

Poor navigation techniques or abilities tend to be a mix of the following:

Human factors: Officers may remember being taught methods and practices in college, but they have never actually seen anyone put them into practice on board ship.

Experience: This is usually negative. Officers find that fixes obtained from visual bearings do not agree with GPS or radar positions.

Knowledge: An ever-increasing number of basic navigational knowledge gaps observed.

En route

During the voyage the assessor can use past navigation incidents, accident investigations and the case studies in this book to help explain why it is important to follow specific aspects of best practice. If the gaps identified are minor then an onboard coaching session may fix the problem there and then. The gaps should still be documented and recorded.

The assessor needs to consider what approach to take if serious non-conformities are found. If it is done properly, an assessment should not be stressful for the professional navigators on board the vessel.

The time an assessor spends on board is crucial. Even an assessment covering just one or two days will clearly have an effect on ship's staff and hours of rest, and care should be taken to ensure it is carried out with minimum disturbance to them. The assessor should be flexible and adapt to the ship's routine, taking that routine into consideration when conducting the assessment.

NI LinkedIn group

❝ We need to establish a culture across the international shipping community which champions the value of a navigation and seamanship heritage developed over centuries with the notion of 'competent independence' at its centre. Assessments should not be viewed as quality assurance by inspection but by benchmarking and professional mentoring. This would give those who need it the opportunity to catch up rather than hide their issues. This seems to be what happens when BRM and other best practices are in evidence in the simulator but left behind when officers go on board. ❞

A navigation assessment should:

- Determine and quantify the navigational risk to the ship and company
- Be systematic, transparent and effective
- Use experienced and trained Master Mariners with command experience, and preferably specifically qualified as assessors
- Include human factors surrounding navigation incidents and bridge management
- Be undertaken during a short sea voyage, including pilotage

Section 2
Navigation assessments – a guide to best practice

- Be a learning and mentoring process carried out in a just atmosphere
- Provide action points, which should be followed up.

The assessor should keep in mind that the objectives of a navigation assessment include understanding the prevailing work culture within the organisation. They should be aware of company policies relating to navigation.

To be truly successful, ship's officers have to volunteer information and to do this the assessor has to be embedded and be regarded as a colleague.

Assessor

66 *I have carried out different assessments for over six years. In my experience as an assessor I have found that I had to help the people to be assessed to be as relaxed as possible before I started work. I explain to them that I am on board to see that the system is working properly and that I am not on board to find fault with anyone, but, on the contrary, to see if there are any flaws in the system.* 99

Pre-assessment for companies

If the assessment is to identify the navigational shortfalls, the process has to give officers an opportunity to improve on practices and make constructive suggestions. The working environment is an ideal place in which to do coaching and mentoring.

Some considerations:

- Independent assessors should be used
- It is the company's systems that are under scrutiny, and the crew's ability to carry them out
- Assessments should be carried out regularly across the fleet, not as spot-checks
- Assessments should be regarded as a learning exercise for shore and sea staff
- Assessments should be part of a continuing system of change and improvement for the company and individuals
- Regular assessments should be held and augmented by unscheduled ones
- Assessment recommendations should be discussed with shore and sea staff and acted upon

- Provide ways for Masters and watchkeepers to suggest improvements to working practices
- Encourage coaching and mentoring
- Operate in a just culture, not a blame culture.

Case study

Hyundai Dominion/Sky Hope collision in East China Sea, June 2004. The vessel's managers had a programme in place for external navigation assessments to monitor performance and provided a standard for the company's internal navigation audits. The programme required independent assessors to travel on vessels for several days, observing procedures and discussing operations with Masters and watchkeepers.

A navigation assessment of this type had not been carried out on the *Hyundai Dominion*, although reports written after assessments had been carried out on similar vessels in the manager's fleet indicated that its navigation assessments were thorough and provided a worthwhile training function for ships' staff. The MAIB found that the limited number of assessments undertaken were unlikely to have given the managers a representative evaluation of navigational safety on board their vessels.

According to the MAIB, navigation assessments of the quality that were undertaken had the potential to ensure that high standards of navigational safety were achieved and maintained.

NI LinkedIn group

66 *I have carried out various navigation assessments and these all showed different weaknesses. Two were on ships of an internationally renowned company operating container ships – and carried out on behalf of the company's head office and insurers. The company was quite dismissive of some of the recommendations, suggesting that they only applied to tankers (including one suggestion to set guidelines for minimum bridge manning scales in various conditions). This was despite them having had a few collisions and groundings. All the assessments showed up the inappropriate use of ECS (non-approved ECDIS). This is very common.* 99

Many companies require Masters to conduct navigation assessments on board merely as a means of 'ticking boxes'. Even if defects or deficiencies are noted, Masters are often pressured not to mention them, because an assessor conducting an external assessment might ask what has been done to rectify the defect. This should be one of the benefits of carrying out an external assessment. Masters should be encouraged and trained in navigation assessments so that they can have a good understanding of the navigation practices on board.

Case study

Oliva grounding on Nightingale Island, March 2011. The last annual internal assessment of *Oliva* by the marine superintendent was held five months before the vessel ran aground. The assessment drew attention to incomplete passage plans. In accordance with the vessel's safety management system, the Master conducted a navigation assessment two months before the grounding. He did not identify any shortcomings nor did he include any observations about improving navigation practices on board. Transport Malta noted that although the company had provided comprehensive guidance and procedures in its SMS to prevent this accident, these were not followed on board. Transport Malta's recommendations included holding unscheduled navigation audits at sea, so as to verify compliance of the company's operational procedures while the vessel is underway.

NI LinkedIn group

❝ *I once told a client CEO of a very large company that I couldn't believe that he only monitored navigation at the annual ISM audit on his large container ships. One small navigation error could wipe out the company. Two weeks later I received a call to say that one of the company's container ships had grounded in the Singapore Strait with significant pollution. From that moment the company introduced regular assessments and close monitoring of navigation, which continue to today.* ❞

Pre-assessment for Masters and watchkeepers

All those in the bridge team have to realise that navigation and navigation assessments are not tick box exercises. Officers need to demonstrate at all times the commitment, motivation and attitude to their tasks that is essential for the safe conduct of their vessel. If this attitude is brought to bear, the navigation assessment will reflect that.

Senior officers should encourage all colleagues to coach and mentor in order to spread good working practices. A navigation assessment should be regarded as part of any officer's continuing professional development (CPD). Suggestions for improvement should be taken positively and acted upon.

NI LinkedIn group

As a Shipmaster I found navigation assessments invaluable as a means to assess deck officers' competence and for determining the status of the bridge as a whole. Regardless of when an assessment was due, I would evaluate officers after a month on board and include a full chart or publication and navigation equipment status assessment as well. Officers would be informed of this on joining and I would encourage them to ask me any questions or request training in areas they thought they might be weak in.

NI LinkedIn group

There was disconnection between theory and practice shown on one vessel. The passage plan had all parallel index lines (PI) marked up on the charts, but PI was not being used for navigation. The officers knew that OCIMF SIRE requires PI, so the lines were marked on the charts to forestall any observation at the next inspection. The technique was not used during the passage, however.

In that instance, the management team knew industry best practice, but decided not to follow it. In the words of the ISM Code, that team lacked the commitment, motivation and attitude to follow best practice.

The assessor decided this indicated an attitude problem rather than any lack of knowledge. He pointed out that it showed that ships' staff are getting good at completing checklists and ensuring that all looks good, at least on paper.

The SMS

Good navigation practice should be contained in a vessel's SMS, but all too often this is not the case. Cynics often say this is because SMSs are written by those who have no experience of the operational world and no understanding of a company's work culture.

In a Nautical Institute London branch technical meeting, 'Watchkeeping Standards – Do Navigation Audits Help?' Carl Durow, loss prevention manager at the London P&I Club, presented a case study of a small container vessel fleet entered in the club. There had been several relatively minor collisions and other navigation incidents in the fleet, but these were increasing, causing concern both to the club and to the owners. To find the root causes, a navigation assessment was carried out with an assessor travelling on board for eight days observing two coastal passages and four pilotage operations. General findings showed poor passage planning, particularly under pilotage, where the bridge team relied too much on the pilot. There was no routine monitoring of Navtex or radio/Sat C weather warnings.

The assessor debriefed those on board and the company adopted the proposed procedures. The subsequent claims record from this fleet reduced dramatically.

At the same meeting, Yusuf Soomro, marine consultant with TMC (Marine), said the key objective of a navigation assessment is to observe the bridge team's performance and interaction during various stages of a passage. The assessor should note navigation practices during arrival, berthing, departure, coastal or ocean passages and watch handovers. Assessments should be performed within a clearly communicated no-blame culture, where any lessons learned, both positive and negative, will be shared throughout the company. This ensures that the assessor will be welcomed on board and will effectively engage with the bridge team. His advice was for assessors to try to make the inspection a learning experience and to discuss the reason why items were highlighted. He said the whole point was to ensure the bridge team understands the reasons behind a requirement; when this is achieved there is usually much better adherence to and support for the practice.

During discussion after the presentations, one member of the audience said that SMS and bridge procedures were critical, so time spent conducting navigation assessments was effort well spent in ensuring procedures were correct. The biggest problem he had identified was Shipmasters accepting work that didn't meet best practice. He said it was most important that bridge procedures are constantly reinforced and for Masters to be certain that best practice is adhered to.

One enemy to best practice is poor time management and the contributor felt that this was an issue that can – and should – be identified through a navigation assessment. He stressed the importance of really engaging with the bridge team, as only then will the benefit of assessments become apparent. A successful assessment will ensure engagement at all levels: assessor, bridge team and company. People need to feel empowered and that they are part of the team.

The use of desktop scenarios using incidents from official accident investigation reports, particularly when discussing Colregs incidents and considering how situations developed, is a useful way of engaging the bridge teams.

The challenges include finding the best ways to measure and assess safety culture, how we can generate a culture within which bridge teams can speak freely, and how to promote constant engagement and self-assessment with the bridge team by understanding their social and work culture.

Case study

Navigator Scorpio grounding, Haisborough Sand, January 2014. The vessel ran aground in restricted waters after the OOW was distracted and lost positional awareness when undertaking passage planning and chart corrections. The passage plan was incomplete and the significant effects of wind and strong tidal streams had not been properly taken into account. Given the proximity to danger, appropriate navigation techniques should have been applied but were not, and manning of the bridge was insufficient.

Some three months before the grounding, with the same crew on board, the marine superintendent conducted a thorough and comprehensive internal assessment over four days. This accurately identified shortcomings in navigation. This assessment recommended that attention be paid to passage-planning and position-fixing methods, as the inexperience of a newly promoted second officer meant that both areas required improvement. Training was provided.

Following the grounding an independent navigation assessment of the vessel was conducted and weaknesses were identified in position-monitoring, passage-planning and the upkeep of charts and publications.

The MAIB concluded that the company and the vessel's Master had not placed a sufficiently high priority on addressing the navigation weaknesses highlighted three months earlier and their actions were insufficient to prevent the failures that led to the grounding.

Herein lies a major problem: often assessments are arranged only after incidents occur. The whole purpose of assessments is to identify problems *before* they become incidents. This requires a major culture change at several levels – in companies, flag states and P&I clubs.

Notice of assessments

According to the NI survey, on being notified an assessment was planned, 26% of those at sea reported reacting very positively and 56% had neutral views. Where assessments were conducted, 42% of shipboard officers said their company gave more than seven days' advance notice of an assessment and 40% reported between three and seven days' notice.

SGCG

66 *Navigational assessments, or other audits for that matter, are not welcome events on board ships. Most of us out at sea regard the assessor as a person prying into our working life at sea.*

The reason is that the shore staff and the ship's staff do not always understand each other. As soon as you see an assessor walking on board the ship the general feeling among the crew is 'Here comes trouble.' 99

Section 3

The assessment

An assessment is not just about completing a checklist. The assessor should observe all aspects of the navigation of the vessel. Observing the relationships and behaviour during a navigational activity is more important than ticking boxes and can usually reveal where something isn't being done that should be. The assessor should avoid focusing on areas of marginal importance while ignoring the most serious risks, which can result from over-reliance on detailed checklists.

Effective navigation assessments will include:

- Pre-departure preparation
- Departure from port with pilot on board
- Coastal and open sea passage
- Pre-arrival preparation and arrival at port with pilot.

It would also be useful to observe anchoring of the vessel, if possible.

This is the ideal for an assessment and should take four or five days, bearing in mind that the assessor also has to rest in between activities.

Positive feedback should be sought from the officers – the assessor should NEVER accept responses that include words such as 'possibly', 'maybe', 'I think so' or 'usually'.

Questions should be of the 'show me', 'how do you', 'where is', 'what if' type. A good way of checking the OOW's knowledge is to ask: "What would you do if…?"

When considering their knowledge of equipment, the assessor can say: "I do not know how to do this. Can you show me how it's done?" To quote Rudyard Kipling, "I kept six honest serving men, they taught me all I know, their names are What, Where, When, Why, How and Who?"

The opening and closing meetings of any assessment are very important and it is no different for a navigation assessment.

SGCG

" Masters should insist on opening and closing meetings with navigation assessors. They should make sure the plan of inspection is clearly defined and reserve the right to intervene should the operation of the vessel require them to do so. At the closing meeting, the assessor should read the report and give the Master the opportunity to comment. "

The opening meeting should be on the bridge if safe navigation and work/rest hours permit. The assessor should set out clearly what will and will not be done and take great care not to undermine the Master's authority,

It should be made very clear that the presence of the assessor in no way affects the duties and responsibilities of the bridge team and they should continue their normal navigation routine. It is absolutely essential that an assessor's presence on the bridge should not interrupt the OOW's work throughout the assessment; activities should be observed as they occur.

During an assessment, the assessor should hold an informal meeting with the Master at the end of each day and brief him on progress. This provides an opportunity to discuss any operational issues that may affect the assessment.

In the closing meeting on board, all watchkeepers should be invited to discuss any observations or findings recorded during the assessment. If time permits, some of these should be closed out while the assessor is on board. The assessor should provide guidance on any of the findings that cannot be closed through lack of time.

Observations and findings need to be supported by objective evidence and agreed by the bridge team. Every non-conformity should be linked to a standard reference, such as STCW, *BPG5*, SOLAS, MLC, instruction manuals and SMS.

The assessor can provide recommendations in areas that may require further improvement. When sharing findings with the crew, it helps if the wording can be agreed between the assessor and the crew.

It is vital to emphasise the positive and, where possible, provide practical solutions. For example, if communication is found to be poor, the assessor could suggest ways that it can be improved.

It should be remembered that it is the company that has requested the assessment, so it is to the company that the assessor must respond. The decision on whether to present findings to the crew will depend upon their reaction to the assessor's presence on board. Usually, it is possible to hold meetings and discuss the findings daily. However, in some cases this may not be practicable, such as when the assessor is leaving as the vessel arrives at a port and there is too little time to hold a closing meeting.

This would be unfortunate, as the closing meeting would help to put things into perspective, bearing in mind the sensibilities of the crew.

NI LinkedIn group

❝ *I debrief discussing the shortcomings which need to be identified, with reasons and explanations. These must not sound like you are imposing your way on them. Over 95% of bridge team members have accepted the recommendations I have proposed and I have seen a major improvement their performance in subsequent assessments.* ❞

The assessor should set some time aside for reviewing:

- Documentation including log book entries, record-keeping, vetting and PSC reports
- Previous assessments and reviews and outcomes
- Accident and incident reports, with any root cause analysis
- Passage plans.

As part of best practice it is recommended to start drafting the report at the end of each day so that the key points and observations are still fresh in the assessor's mind. On completion of the assessment, the assessor will have a draft report ready to be shared with the bridge team.

When the assessment is complete, the assessor should compile a final written report to the company with a summary of the findings, observations, positive points, any corrective actions required and proposed follow-up actions.

OOW – key to the assessment

Assessing the capability and competence of the OOW can give a good idea of the standard of navigation on board the vessel. Even with today's sophisticated, integrated advanced navigation equipment, the OOW must still apply the basics – adherence to the Colregs is paramount. Does the OOW apply the Master's standing orders and company procedures for passing distances, for instance? Or does he rely on the CPA given by the electronic equipment as being an adequate safety margin?

It might appear to the OOW that there is sufficient time to assess a situation and take appropriate action. However, the situation can become dangerous very quickly, requiring rapid decision-making. A well-trained bridge team will mitigate these potential dangers by taking early action, as appropriate. Risk of collision or grounding will then be reduced. Use of modern equipment will greatly aid the OOW's decision-making and, combined with the OOW's professionalism, will demonstrate the level of navigation on board.

Case study

Hamburg grounding, Sound of Mull, May 2015. The ship grounded because the bridge team did not recognise their vessel was approaching from an unsafe direction. Serious shortcomings in the conduct of navigation on board contributed to this lack of awareness, further compounded by the lack of teamwork between officers on the bridge. The completed passage plan was missing several important points, and when the ship was delayed no attempt was made to amend it, nor was an alternative anchorage planned. The MAIB noted: "Had the company audit examined the navigation processes on *Hamburg* it would have identified many of the failings discussed in this report. The company could then have put in place suitable corrective measures to bring these up to the required standard."

This case could be used as a basis for discussion with the bridge team, specifically to consider any lack of detail in the passage plan. Wheel-over positions, no-go areas, abort points, clearing lines and navigation warnings were not marked on the charts. Also, positions were plotted infrequently at irregular times and denoted by a wide variety of symbols.

Assessment procedure

The criteria form in Section 6 on page 73 should be completed and the scoring summarised so that it can be used in the company's KPI system. This figure can also be used to show continuous improvement (or not) in subsequent assessments.

The assessment areas should be in line with this criteria document.

Passage planning

This procedure will be specified as part of the SMS. In any case, the assessor should expect to see three distinct stages in the passage plan:

- Preliminary
- Appraisal and risk assessment
- Planning.

This is then followed by monitoring of the plan during the voyage in ocean, coastal and pilotage waters, all of which should be planned from berth to berth. Particular attention should be paid to areas of high traffic density, shallow water or pilotage waters, making sure the plan incorporates appropriate margins of safety and contingency for unexpected incidents.

The assessor should develop open questions based on the key points for each section, as set out below.

Preliminary

Master and navigating officer discuss and establish route, owner's and charterer's requirements, weather routeing, voyage distance and fuel requirements. This will probably have been completed before the assessor joins the vessel. The assessor should therefore find out from the Master and navigator the procedure for this stage, including the Master's overriding authority in line with company SMS and SOLAS Chapter V.

Section 3

Navigation assessments – a guide to best practice

Appraisal and risk assessment

The assessor should observe this stage to ensure the navigator has collected all relevant information from publications and acted upon it. This will include:

- List of lights, radio signals, tide tables and sailing directions
- Risk assessment of the voyage and route plan
- Checking for no-go areas due to other circumstances such as piracy
- Establishing draught and under-keel clearance (UKC)
- Assembling and verifying that charts needed for the voyage (whether electronic or paper) are corrected, up to date and available
- Ensuring all ENCs are licensed
- Identifying any traffic separation schemes
- Making allowance for environmental considerations such as emission control areas (ECAs) and areas where discharge is permitted or prohibited under MARPOL Annex V
- Evaluating distance off coastlines and dangers
- Plotting particularly sensitive sea areas (PSSAs)
- Ascertaining the pilot embarkation/disembarkation positions
- Making contingency plans.

It is unlikely to be possible to complete the berth-to-berth passage plan, as information about transit with the pilot on board to or from the berth is unlikely to be obtained in advance. Even so, this part of the process should be covered using all available information, noting that it may change during the voyage. If the crew accesses the port's website for these details, the assessor should warn that, however useful it may be, the information – as with any other information obtained from websites – should be treated with caution, as it may not be kept up to date.

Planning

For this section, the assessor should expect the navigating officer to:

- Review the plotted course ensuring all risks are mitigated
- Mark no-go areas, particularly for tidal sections
- Mark safe waters for any deviations including avoidance of collisions in restricted depths

- Make checks at appropriate scale for the area
- Make a visual inspection of the route on the chart.
- Follow these procedures every time even if on a regular route, as the various publications may have been amended.

Pre-departure meetings

These should be held with all bridge team members and the chief engineer. The assessor will be looking to see if these officers are briefed on the passage plan and understand the intended route and procedures necessary for transit.

Important points to note in the discussion are:

- Wheel-over positions
- The use of parallel indexing
- Abort points
- Any actions necessary after abort point if unplanned actions occur
- Safe anchorages
- Position-fixing methods
- Changeover to low-sulphur fuel for transit through ECAs.

The assessor should observe how the briefing for the passage plan is conducted, noting whether it includes an opportunity for members of the bridge team to query or comment on any part of the plan that they do not fully understand. Adequate time must be allowed for this briefing, which should also consider any variation from the routine running of the vessel. This might include additional watches, engine room on standby and anchor party requirements.

The briefing should clarify objectives and ensure the team understands the plan before the voyage starts. The assessor can use interview questions to determine if this has been done.

Monitoring the voyage

The assessor will be observing during the voyage to see how the officers are following the passage plan.

Case study

Arslan II grounding, Arklow Bank, January 2014. This report concluded that standard procedures for navigation and management of a vessel were not followed during the voyage. The vessel's movements were based on reliance on a small-scale chart and compounded by the improper use of unofficial tide tables. The interval between position-fixing points was inadequate for a vessel operating in coastal waters.

The incident highlighted the need for vessels to use other means of navigation in coastal waters to verify their position and the effects of tides, currents and winds on the course made good. These could be visual compass bearings, radar bearings and ranges from fixed objects.

On completion of the voyage, there should be a debriefing meeting, with relevant team members, discussing what went well and what, if any, problems were encountered.

Alternative passage plan

Not all voyages can have alternative routes, but, if applicable, the assessor should discuss the criteria when planning alternative routes with the navigator.

No-go areas and abort points

The assessor should verify that watchkeepers understand the concept of no-go areas and abort points. These must be clearly marked on paper charts and ENCs. See also UK MAIB Report no 12/2016 (*Hamburg*) in this section, page 32, and Transport Malta Report 14/2012 (*Oliva*) in Section 2, page 24.

Equipment tested, status verified pre-sailing and arrival

Observations will include the way checks are carried out and recorded, and cover ship's staff awareness of procedures to change from auto to manual steering and *vice versa*. SOLAS requirements need to be highlighted and a full demonstration carried out.

Bridge team organisation – manning levels

The assessor will need to check and verify the company's SMS to ensure conformance with watchkeeping arrangements under various conditions. The bridge should be properly manned at all times and, in areas of restricted passage, restricted visibility, adverse weather and extended pilotages such as river passages, crewing should be organised to allow for adequate relief and rest. Requirements for when the Master should be on the bridge can also be discussed. This should be in the fleet regulations.

Case study

Paula C/Darya Gayatri collision in Dover Strait, December 2013. The *Paula C*'s very inexperienced OOW had not developed sufficient competency to keep a bridge watch in the Dover Strait at night on his own and was not supported by an additional lookout. The MAIB said the Master's decision to allow an inexperienced officer to keep the bridge watch was ill-judged and contrary to international requirements. The OOW was not using the available electronic aids effectively and lost situational awareness. The MAIB judged that the Master treated the passage through the Dover Strait no differently from a passage in open water.

Effective use of bridge equipment

Masters and watchkeeping officers should be completely familiar with all the navigation and communication equipment on board. The assessor can check that watchkeepers understand the status, capabilities and limitations of the equipment. If the initial observation indicates that the bridge team is highly effective in this, the assessor should observe how they perform over the voyage.

If watchkeepers' use of equipment is poor, then the assessor needs to probe further. They should confirm that bridge equipment meets the regulatory requirements set out in SOLAS Chapter V and that checks are made. These checks will be made on a range of equipment, including:

- Sensor inputs to ECDIS
- Gyro heading on radars
- Settings and cross-checking GNSS
- Echo sounder against charted depths

Section 3
Navigation assessments – a guide to best practice

- Changeover from manual to auto steering (and *vice versa*)
- Off-course alarm
- Speed log
- Telegraph logger
- Course recorder.

In addition, the assessor should find out whether:

- AIS dynamic and static data are updated when details are amended
- The bridge navigational watch alarm system (BNWAS) is set up properly with lock protection under control of the Master
- Procedures for saving VDR data are understood; all OOWs must know the correct operation and action in emergency and what is saved to the VDR.

Case study

Sundstraum/Kapitan Lus collision off Copenhagen, July 2009. Among other findings, the AIB found that the operators of the *Sundstraum* allowed the ship's officers three days to familiarise themselves with the bridge equipment. This was probably insufficient, as the bridge crew members directly involved in the accident demonstrated that they were not familiar with the functioning of the autopilot changeover or the emergency steering equipment.

Monitoring instruments

The assessor should find out whether watchkeepers are familiar with the performance, efficiency and testing of the bridge equipment. Do they understand the procedures in place for reporting equipment malfunction to the Master, DPA and flag and PSC administrations (if required)? The process and contingency planning for equipment failure should be observed.

Traffic appreciation

The way in which traffic management is handled on board the ship in open sea and congested areas should be observed. In coastal and congested areas, collision avoidance and position-fixing is much more complex than in open sea. The assessor should discuss with officers how they use their judgement in this area. Key points to be considered are:

- Correct application of Colregs
- Situational awareness
- Position-fixing
- Course alterations
- Interaction between OOW and Master
- Posting additional lookouts during restricted visibility
- Use of AIS and ARPA
- Understanding of when to call the Master
- Reducing speed if required
- Concept of safe speed and deviation from route
- Use of lookout as appropriate.

The assessor should also discuss with the OOW the dangers of using VHF when applying Colregs. In some of the case studies in this book, using VHF in an attempt to avoid a collision has had the opposite effect – see *CMA CGM Florida/Chou Shan* and *Ever Smart/Alexandra 1*, pages 41 and 42 later in this section.

Case study

Katre/Statengracht collision in the Baltic Sea, February 2013. The immediate cause was an unclear assessment of the risk of collision in a dynamic environment with no proper lookout and a failure to follow bridge procedures.

A better assessment of the risk of collision would have been a vital support to the OOWs on both vessels. The situation on board the two ships reflected critical factors that shaped the decisions of the OOWs including the uncertain and dynamic environment. Several ships were competing for the attention of the OOWs. Feedback loops were limited and unclear for communication within the ships and between the ships.

Application of Colregs

The assessor should observe application of Colregs during the assessment and discuss with OOWs their understanding of:

- Safe speed
- Traffic separation
- Action to avoid close quarter situations
- Responsibility of a power-driven vessel
- Restricted visibility.

Case study

Spring Glory/Josephine Mærsk collision in approaches to Singapore Strait, June 2012. In the approaches to the Singapore Strait there is often a high risk of collision. In this case, the two ships were in a crossing situation, with *Spring Glory* as the give-way ship and *Josephine Mærsk* as the stand-on ship.

On *Spring Glory* the OOW acknowledged the presence of *Josephine Mærsk* in due time. However, the officer's focus was on crossing traffic from the starboard side, ships at anchor and a forthcoming altering of course. He delayed taking action because he believed the situation would develop more favourably than it did. He hoped the *Josephine Mærsk* would alter its course and resolve the situation. By the time he realised the seriousness of the situation, his attempts to avoid a collision were too late.

Track management

This part of the assessment checks watchkeepers' understanding of those areas where the ship may safely deviate from its track and the limits of this safe water. The way in which the track is resumed after deviation to avoid collision should then be discussed.

Communication management

Effective communication can be difficult and the potential for misunderstanding is great. Standard marine communication phrases should be used. The ultimate aim is to transmit and receive information so that each party knows what the other is saying and meaning. The assessor will observe how team members interact with each other and with outside agencies.

Case study

CMA CGM Florida/Chou Shan collision, East China Sea, March 2013. There were two second officers on the bridge of *CMA CGM Florida* at the time of the collision: a Filipino who was the OOW and a Chinese national who had just joined the vessel and was on the bridge for familiarisation. Discussions took place between the vessels to negotiate a passing situation contrary to Rule 15 of the Colregs. The Chinese second officer conducted this conversation with the *Chou Shan* in Mandarin. Translation of the conversation to the Filipino officer was incomplete and he was unaware of the actions agreed in Mandarin to avoid collision. Consequently, the Filipino second officer was not fully aware of the situation and action was taken too late to prevent collision.

Good communicators reflect on and discuss the significance of information; they make provision for other options and potential outcomes, and communicate those options. Good communicators are also decisive and have clear goals. Poor communicators are aggressive or unresponsive if their plan is questioned; they do not discuss potential problems and show insensitivity to the impact of language, culture or disability on communication (see Section 5).

The assessor should see evidence that a working language has been established on the bridge in accordance with SOLAS Chapter V/14.4. The working language should be English. This is a relatively non-hierarchical language and can help overcome some cultural elements of poor relationships.

Observe any signs that may indicate the likelihood of a breakdown in communication especially if team members are from different backgrounds or from different areas of the same country. During pilotage, communication between the pilot and other bridge team members should be observed as well as the communication between the ship and port control and/or VTS.

Case study

Ever Smart/Alexandra 1 collision at Jebel Ali, February 2015. The collision resulted from the vessels' Masters having differing perceptions of how the vessels would pass each other. A passing arrangement was not agreed or communicated before the collision and the actions of both Masters were based on assumptions.

The reliance of *Alexandra 1*'s Master on scanty VHF information and the failure of *Ever Smart*'s Master to keep a proper lookout and monitor *Alexandra 1*'s movement were crucial to this accident. A lack of an agreed plan and effective communication, coordination and monitoring were significant factors that contributed to the flaws in the situational awareness of *Ever Smart*'s and *Alexandra 1*'s Masters.

Anticipation and decision-making

The assessor should observe actions by officers on watch for collision avoidance and dangers, the way they take effective action, the factors they consider and how they undertake decision-making.

Situational awareness

Crew members' understanding of the level of situational awareness and possible reasons for distractions such as fatigue and work overload should be assessed.

According to *ICS Bridge Procedures Guide* (5th Edition, 2016), situational awareness is an appreciation of what is happening around the ship. This includes knowing where the ship is, where it is planned to be, and whether any other vessel, event or conditions developing in the vicinity pose a risk to the safety of the ship.

It is essential that there are no distractions or any non-essential activity on the bridge such as music playing. This would be clearly heard during the playback of the voyage data recorder (VDR). To avoid distractions on the bridge when the ship is in a high-risk area, some companies use a traffic light system to restrict admission to the bridge. Green is normal, yellow is moderate alert and red is high alert when bridge entry is restricted to key personnel.

Case study

Tongala/Bo Spring collision off Philippines coast, May 2015. The report concluded, among other things, that neither OOW had an accurate situation awareness of the dynamic context around his ship. The OOW of the *Tongala* was working in the chartroom preparing the passage plan for the next voyage until the collision occurred. The VDR recorded activity in the chartroom throughout including the opening and closing of chart drawers, which showed the OOW was not looking out at the developing situation.

Case study

Rena grounding on Astrolabe Reef, October 2011. This report observed that watchkeepers must be fully aware of where a ship is at all times and of all factors that affect the ship's progress, or are likely to in the immediate future. Knowing about environmental factors such as wind, sea, current and tide is important, as is knowledge of the status of the navigation equipment used to direct and monitor the progress of the ship.

Bridge team management (BTM)

The primary goal of BTM is the elimination of single-person errors. The assessor should discuss this aim in detail with the Master and officers and ensure that they have a good conceptual understanding of team management and the elimination of 'single-person errors'. All members of the bridge team should be aware of all vessel operations.

According to *BPG5*, effective BTM builds a team that has a plan, is well briefed, works effectively and is able to develop and maintain good situational awareness. This team should then be able to anticipate dangerous situations and recognise the development of a sequence of errors, taking action to break any chain of errors and avert emergencies.

Response to stress

The watchkeepers should be observed and their actions and response when working under stressful conditions noted.

Delegation of duties

The assessor should discuss with the Master how and why duties are delegated to officers, including giving and receiving the con of the ship.

Confidence

The assessor should use his own experience to judge how confident the officers are in their ability to manage navigation.

Pilotage

Pilots are a critical part of the bridge team, which is responsible for helping the pilot to work within that team. The assessor should observe the Master/pilot exchange (MPX) and note what information is exchanged. To be able to monitor the pilot's actions, the Master and crew ought to have a thorough understanding of the pilot's intentions and plans for the ship's movements and be able to clarify any issues that have been identified during the preparation of the onboard voyage plan.

Case study

Capri/Brightoil Legend allision Singapore, July 2015. The immediate cause of the accident was ineffective teamwork between the bridge team and the pilot. There was no evidence of any formal exchange of information on pilotage or the anchoring position, and the Master did not query the deviation from the original anchorage position. Essential information on the pilot's intended passage or anchoring operations was overlooked, other than a note "as per passage plan".

Although the *Capri* was not going to an alongside berth, it was in a dynamic environment in the Singapore anchorage. The Transport Malta report shows that the lack of monitoring and situational awareness on board *Capri* contributed to the allision with the anchored *Brightoil Legend*.

The pilotage segment of any passage plan must be considered a dynamic process and be capable of being updated quickly. The MPX should incorporate any amendments to the pilot-to-berth section of the passage plan. This should include:

- Transit to or from the berth, the agreed route, speed, timing, tidal conditions, abort points and contingency plans
- If tugs are required, the number, type and power of tugs, and the place where tugs will meet the vessel
- Up-to-date information on the berth including limitations, restrictions and the mooring plan.

Masters and officers must always remain vigilant, professional and in control of their ship's progress during this critical phase of the voyage.

Case study

Maersk Garonne grounding, Fremantle, February 2015. The investigation found that bridge resource management was not effectively implemented on board. Neither OOW was briefed on the key details discussed during the MPX. Therefore, the OOWs were unaware that the courses marked on the ship's chart were not to be followed. As a result, the ship's bridge team members were not fully engaged in the pilotage and were unable to develop and maintain a shared understanding and mental model of the plan and expectations for the pilotage as it progressed. Their ability to maintain situational awareness was compromised by not knowing what the plan was. As a result, they were not actively engaged in the pilotage and were unable to assist in the detection and management of errors or deviations from the plan.

Pilots are the waterway experts and Masters are the vessel experts. Masters and pilots, working together, are central to effective vessel team performance. They assist one another by providing or verifying waterway and vessel information.

Case study

Overseas Reymar allision, San Francisco, January 2013. The vessel's allision with the San Francisco–Oakland Bay Bridge in San Francisco happened after the Master was talking on the phone during a critical navigation phase. This adversely affected the safety of the vessel's transit. By removing himself from the team because of these phone conversations, the Master was unable to assist and oversee the pilot effectively and did not realise that the vessel was no longer on a safe course.

The assessor should check that the Master and officers are satisfied with the planned transit and berthing and unberthing manoeuvres. The co-operation of the Master and bridge team includes confirmation of the language to be used throughout so that helm and engine orders can be quickly and properly acknowledged and carried out.

An accurately completed pilot card gives pilots all the essential basic information to build their own picture for the passage and any manoeuvres that will be carried out. It can be supplemented in discussion with the Master and the bridge team.

Case study

Doric Chariot grounding, North Queensland, July 2002. During the passage under pilotage there were several opportunities for the pilot to take rest. When he did eventually sit down intending to rest, he fell asleep. There were no clear instructions to the OOW regarding the course and when the pilot should be called. The OOW did not properly understand the pilot's intentions and did not express any doubt, which he should have done. A qualified and competent officer should have recognised the intention from the chart. The OOW did not fix the ship's positions at intervals that were consistent with safe navigation and did not adjust the ship's course to follow the route drawn on the chart. When the pilot was called, he recognised that the vessel was in a dangerous position, but the action taken was too late to prevent grounding on the reef.

Integration of pilot

It is well established that the pilot and the bridge team should have a common view of how a voyage will unfold. It is also important that good communication between the pilot and the bridge team is sustained throughout the voyage. When the pilot and bridge officers share a common picture of the voyage, they can each monitor the progress of manoeuvres from their different vantage points on the vessel, so reducing the possibility of single-point failure.

Watchkeepers should have a clear understanding that the pilot is part of bridge team and should recognise the importance of sharing all relevant information with the pilot. As P&I club reports show, one out of 10 navigation accidents take place with a pilot on board so it is important that a transparent system prevails. The Master and his team should share information about the malfunctioning of any of the bridge equipment.

Case study

Atlantic Blue gounding, Torres Strait, February 2009. A coastal pilot was on board for the intended eastbound transit of the Torres Strait. The passage progressed normally, but due to the prevailing wind and tide conditions the vessel was 1 mile south of the planned track. A number of small heading adjustments were made but none was effective, and *Atlantic Blue*'s bow grounded on a sandy shoal near Kirkcaldie Reef. The findings by the ATSB showed that position-fixing and track-monitoring methods used by the bridge team were not consistently accurate because they did not make the most effective and appropriate use of radar and Global Positioning System equipment.

BRM was ineffective and the functional efficiency of the bridge progressively declined in the absence of a shared mental model and adequate communication between members of the bridge team.

Monitoring of pilot

Watchkeepers must understand that having a pilot on board does not relieve them of their responsibilities. They need to monitor ship's position continuously and be ready to intervene if they are concerned about, for instance, excessive speed or missing a course alteration. However competent the pilot may be, the bridge team must monitor the progress of the vessel on the chart or ECDIS. A pilot should not be concerned about being asked questions regarding the position of the vessel or the planned course.

If the pilot gives instructions to a tug in a different language from that used on board the bridge team should ensure that the pilot clarifies how the tug will be used and the instructions given to it.

Case study

Bonden/Asian Breeze collision off Malmö, March 2015. The tug *Bonden* collided with *Asian Breeze* during berthing at Malmö, Sweden. The accident was caused by a lack of planning and poor implementation of the tug/ship connection procedure. The pilot was not informed of the malfunctioning bow thruster at the MPX. The pilot communicated with the tug in Swedish, which he translated for the ship's staff, but the conditions meant it was hard for them to follow the sequence of events.

Master's standing and night orders

The assessor should check that the Master's standing orders are written clearly and that they are understood by the watchkeepers. They should set out the chain of command, state how instructions are given on the bridge and responded to, and make clear how bridge team members are to bring safety concerns to the notice of the Master.

They need to include required key points from company standing orders such as minimum levels for visibility, CPA and TCPA, dependent on the stage of the voyage including open passage, coastal passage and high-risk areas.

Master's night orders should include key points to reinforce the passage plan such as the visibility expected, minimum CPA to be observed, and any temporary deviation from voyage plans anticipated such as the expectation of crossing traffic and concentrations of fishing boats. They should also say whether there will be a need for extra lookouts and/or manual steering, what to do if reduction of speed is required, the use of main engines and when to call the Master.

Relevant ship handling

The assessment should make reference to any lack of opportunities for demonstrating shiphandling. If time permits, the assessor should discuss with the Master and chief officer key areas of shiphandling such as the pivot point, transverse thrust effect on the vessel, squat effect, precautions during anchoring and the manoeuvring diagram.

Overall navigation safety

Observations should ensure that all key aspects are covered, particularly watchkeeping procedures, watch handovers, managing the bridge watch and maintaining a proper lookout. The assessor should collect evidence of both good and poor procedures.

Key elements of safe manning levels should be checked, along with safe conduct of navigation, compliance with MARPOL and minimising impact on the environment, effective communication and familiarisation, sound shipboard operational procedures, and robust and practised emergency responses.

Watch handover procedure

The assessor should observe the process of handover and takeover of the watch and the logbook entries. It is important to check whether the watchkeeper reads the Master's night orders, which should also be made clear verbally so that they are recorded on the VDR.

Familiarity with ECDIS

The assessor should satisfy himself that all bridge team members have undergone type-specific familiarisation on the ECDIS on board in addition to receiving generic training. *Industry Guidelines for ECDIS Familiarisation*, published by The Nautical Institute, should be used.

Cyber-security

Increasingly, ships are connected to the internet. The company should have an appropriate cyber-security awareness programme in place. The assessor should establish from ship's staff their awareness of cyber-security and cyber-hygiene. A useful publication, freely available, *The Guidelines on Cyber Security Onboard Ships* (see Further Reading, page 82), is intended to develop understanding and awareness of key aspects of cyber security. The topic is also covered in issue 12 of The Nautical Institute's free magazine, *The Navigator*. On the bridge, ship's staff should be aware that even bridge systems that are not connected to any other networks may be vulnerable, as removable media are often used to update such systems from other onboard networks.

Navigation instructions, procedures, checklists and documents on the bridge

It is a fact of life nowadays that bridge procedures come complete with a checklist. The assessor should monitor the use of checklists and ensure that they are appropriate for the procedure being carried out, noting if any are missing or out of date. In discussion with the bridge team, the assessor should verify that all members of the team are familiar with those in use, ensuring that the latest versions of checklists are used. This may be a good opportunity to discuss the practical application of SMS procedures and the need to avoid ship's staff being overburdened with procedures and checklists.

SGCG

66 It doesn't help much when the records and documentation are deliberately falsified. To detect that this has occurred you first need an accident to justify the cost and time for a full forensic investigation to discover the breakdown, and this is beyond a time-pressed assessor's routine scope. 99

Standard publications

The bridge team's familiarity with the contents of the bridge technical library. This should include the latest editions of appropriate publications in accordance with the company's SMS manual, including Nautical Institute publications.

Entries in log books

The assessment should cover key entries such as the course steered, compass error verification, course alteration, change of con, watch handover and takeover, fire and security rounds and the weather experienced as set out in SOLAS Chapter V Regulation 28 and MSC Circ. A916(22).

Transfer of con

The assessor will check for evidence on how the transfer of con is conducted especially between the Master and OOW and pilots (during long pilotage areas). These need to be completed clearly, in closed-loop style, and recorded on VDR. Appropriate entries should be made in the log and movement books.

If an alteration of course or anti-collision manoeuvre is taking place or is imminent, it is important for the assessor to note whether the watch and con handover is deferred until after the action has been completed.

Case study

Vega Sagittarius grounding off Greenland, August 2012. After sailing from the port of Nuuk, the navigation watch changed four times between the Master and the chief officer within approximately 40 minutes. At one point the chief officer was in doubt whether he was on watch because it was now after 08.00, the time when the third officer usually held the watch. The third officer did not admit to having had the watch at any time before the grounding. The different tasks of the members of the bridge team had been loosely defined and the way in which the change of the watch was carried out caused a loss of information about forthcoming navigation and about the precautions to be taken.

Fatigue, hours of work and rest

A check should be made that the Master uses the passage plan to anticipate areas of high workload and risk and set manning levels appropriately. Manning of the engine room, if required on UMS vessels, also needs to be taken into account.

Compass errors

It is important to ensure that compasses are compared before sailing and that compass error is verified at least once during the watch. If OOWs are unable to verify compass error, they should make a log book entry stating "error unobtainable".

Management of navigation warnings

The assessor should verify that company procedures on navigation warnings are being followed, including receiving and recording. Checks should be made on the way the voyage plan is updated, including plotting relevant navigation warnings on ECDIS and paper charts.

Familiarity with emergency/contingency plans

A discussion with the Master and other officers will ascertain their familiarity with the company's contingency planning including bridge equipment failure. For example, are drills conducted for loss of GNSS? Is the OOW aware when to call the Master? It is important that the bridge team is familiar with the Ship Oil Pollution Emergency Plan (SOPEP) manual.

Lighting

The assessor should consider the light conditions during the hours of darkness, especially the lighting used in the bridge and adjacent area. Is equipment lighting (ECDIS, radar etc.) adjusted to meet circumstances? The crew should be aware of The Nautical Institute's book *Human Performance and Limitation for Mariners*.

End-of-voyage briefing

This provides the opportunity for bridge teams to review the strengths of their passage plans and weaknesses, make suggestions for improved safety or communications and improve team problem-solving skills. Downloads from the

VDR should be used if possible. Lessons learned from review discussions can help in planning better and safer voyages in future. Reviews may be delayed by the involvement in port activities of the Master and officers.

Training

The assessor should discuss with the Master and officers the onboard perception of their company's training policy (including refresher training) on BTM, BRM, shiphandling, ECDIS and collision avoidance.

Maintaining an anchor watch

As and when there is an opportunity, the assessor should observe how an anchor watch is maintained – for this, refer to ICS *BPG5*.

Case study

Wes Janine/Stenberg collision off Brunsbüttel, January 2014. The report concluded that greater care should have been taken in the choice of anchorage. Available anchorages were not discussed in sufficient detail nor were influencing factors such as engine notice, ratio of ship's draught to depth of water, holding ground, anchor holding capacity and currents and tide. The officers in charge of both ships were distracted by other duties or not fully aware of the potential dangers and no additional lookout had been placed. They did not make full use of the alarm settings on the radars, and it was only when the *Wes Janine* had drifted so close to the *Stenberg* that the danger was noticed – too late for any options to avoid collision.

GMDSS equipment

GMDSS watchkeeping and log-keeping should be discussed and observations made of any tests conducted on the equipment and handling of false distress alerts.

Security awareness

The Master and officers need to be able to show awareness of their ship's security arrangements and these arrangements should comply with their ship's security plan.

The assessor should ensure they show good situational awareness when navigating in a reporting area, designated risk area or in an area where the security level has been raised. They should be able to identify threats and put in place effective protection of their ship in a timely manner.

Accident, collision and salvage

If time permits, the assessor should discuss company procedures dealing with post-accident management. Talking primarily with the Master, the assessor should observe their familiarity with company contingency plans and bridge procedures dealing with accidents, collisions and salvage, including knowledge and understanding of Lloyd's Open Form. The SMS should contain clear reference to the Master's overriding authority.

Mentoring

The opportunity should be taken during the assessment to see how mentoring is conducted on the vessel, observing how the Master spends time with officers. Guidance is given in The Nautical Institute publication *Mentoring at Sea – the 10 minute challenge* by André Le Goubin.

Captain Le Goubin says:

66 *Masters do not spend enough time with their junior officers, getting to know them, chatting with them and gradually getting to know their strengths and weaknesses. We have chained Masters to their desks to the point that they often don't visit the bridge at all during navigation watches. Frequently Masters only visit the bridge to send or receive messages and if they can do this from their desks, removing that need. I have even seen an ECDIS repeater at a Master's desk so in principle he only goes to the bridge when he identifies a problem that is not being solved to his satisfaction.* 99

Section 4

Post-assessment

There are many compelling reasons for companies to invest in navigation assessments. It is easy to make a business case for them as the value of the assessment findings goes beyond the continuing improvement of the bridge team.

An assessment is a learning event for both the assessor and the assessed, providing opportunity for improvement. A navigation assessment should add value in terms of learned competencies, fresh insights and new resources. The assessor should not fall into the trap of looking for violations and human failures. An assessment will not be successful merely because the assessor found problems, deficiencies or non-compliance; they need to offer fresh insight. Negative findings on their own merely damage morale and can make the ship's staff feel insecure.

The assessor should therefore aim to help to improve the skills of the bridge team using BRM techniques that can be easily integrated into onboard working. Wherever possible, they should congratulate the bridge team on what has gone well and encourage them to further improvement. The focus should be on how good practices are carried out, where human performance is seen as a solution, not the problem.

Assessment helps to ensure that any gaps between shore-based training and actual practice at sea are adequately addressed. Shore-based training establishments should be given feedback on errors and shortcomings observed at sea, so that training can be improved as appropriate.

NI LinkedIn group

I doubt that assessments encourage many people; in my experience all the connotations are negative. However, most people have a competitive streak and that can be harnessed to good effect. If they can be shown a better way they will generally use it. People will follow procedures they value, and much can be done to redress the poorly trained this way. That's not the assessment process, but it can most effectively follow on from it, when undertaken by the right person. The positive critique which looks at what can be improved rather than what is wrong encourages looking for solutions. 99

To provide constructive feedback the assessor should:

- Be specific – refer to exact patterns of behaviour when discussing both good and poor performance
- Be constructive – help to provide solutions for areas that require attention.

Assessment findings add value to companies in several ways:

- Superintendents and higher management can compare SMS requirements with audit findings
- Upgrade or amend the SMS on navigation
- Identify further instructions or training for equipment on board
- Improve planning and execution of voyages
- Improve safety of navigation
- Observe trends in navigation practice where management intervention is required
- Highlight good and bad aspects of onboard systems
- Highlight design implications and bridge ergonomics; for instance, noting that the echo sounder is inaccessible or not readily available to the OOW
- Give an overall view of the safe navigation of the vessel.

The company should have procedures to address these findings and a timeframe for compliance. Companies derive most benefit from including findings from navigation assessments in a continuous improvement programme and analysing results across the fleet. These may be used to identify areas for improvements, update the SMS and so improve the safety of navigation.

NI LinkedIn group

66 *I believe that the core purpose of assessments – internal or external – is to improve systems. Unless we find the deficiencies we cannot do a gap analysis – and without a gap analysis we cannot work on corrective or preventive actions. In a navigation assessment, some basic gaps would be visible on the spot and ideally a short training*

or briefing then should clear any misconceptions. We should embrace the navigation assessment as a coaching opportunity and a forum to initiate discussions about bridge procedures and practices with watchkeepers. 🔊🔊

Unsafe behaviour caused by a lack of training or complacency can be easily addressed if it is brought to light. Experience has shown that if unsafe behaviour is pointed out in a positive manner, it is less likely to be repeated.

In the NI survey, 84% of assessors said they believed navigation assessments are used to improve performance on the bridge. However, only 40% of the shipboard respondents said an assessment led to changes in bridge procedures.

Other respondents said that assessments often serve as an effective follow-up to past training. Although assessments occasionally identify shortcomings, they also positively reinforce good practices, these respondents said. While new procedures are often adopted following the recommendations from the assessment, 27% said they saw no changes as a result of an assessment, and one pointed out that changes lasted only a short time – "until the assessor leaves".

NI LinkedIn group

🔊🔊 *I sometimes feel part of my role as a pilot is to act as a sympathetic ear for a Master's problems. One of the most consistent complaints is about assessments. I think everybody at sea considers assessments necessary, but to be of benefit the assessor should instruct rather than criticise. Too often though, the ship's staff feel the assessor is just on board to score points and throw their weight around.* 🔊🔊

One benefit of a navigation assessment is to act as a forum that prompts a discussion with watchkeepers about issues such as the Colregs, keeping a good lookout, use of visual bearings to determine risk of collision and the benefit of early and substantial action to avoid close quarters situations. The onboard assessor, whether internal or external, should be involved in this process as this will ensure that the best practice the company wants its staff to apply on board is consistent with the teachings of the training provider.

Added value

SGCG

❝ We recently had an external navigation assessment on board one of our vessels. The company contracted to conduct the assessment recommended five days to complete all aspects. The assessor did the usual physical check and checklist of the equipment and procedures then sat with each of the officers in turn and went through their knowledge of all aspects of bridge watchkeeping and of the equipment used. He included an aspect of the old UK oral exam which turned out to be one of the most valuable aspects of the assessment. What was even more useful was the presence of additional officers on board so we captured a large cross-section of our staff. The internal navigation assessments had picked up nothing at all, as they were based on completing a checklist, which from my previous experience is all that companies want. ❞

Undesirable practice

One Shipmaster was rather scathing about how his company reacted to the results of an internal assessment:

❝ We Masters follow ISM, we implement and at last we review it, but staff sitting in offices get annoyed if we send them the true picture of any assessment including a navigation assessment. After receiving the assessment report from ships the HQSE department catches the marine and technical superintendents concerned to inquire about the outcome of assessment. Some superintendents appreciate it but others get annoyed. ❞

Just culture

A just culture policy is an essential part of modern vessel operations and contributes to a positive health and safety culture. The policy should clearly set out expectations for adherence to and enforcement of procedures in the workplace and recognise performance that exceeds company expectations. Where performance falls below expectations it should be understood that it may not always be the fault of the seafarer.

According to the 2015 edition of the *Code of Safe Working Practices for Merchant Seafarers*, management is responsible for providing support, training and resources so seafarers gain competence to undertake tasks to the required standard. It provides transparent and fair processes and appropriate support to manage behaviour that falls below expectations.

Unlike unacceptable behaviour, honest mistakes and human error should not be punished in a just culture. On the other hand, a just culture can encourage compliance with regulations and procedures, promote safe operating practices and support the development of evaluation programmes.

Seafarers should be encouraged to take responsibility for their actions and management should reward behaviour that exceeds expectations. The policy will need to reflect that firm action may be needed in circumstances where, despite management having provided training or guidance, poor performance still persists.

A just culture expects willing participation from all employees, a strong reporting culture, individual responsibility and organisational accountability and a clear framework for performance management.

Mentoring

If training doesn't translate into improved performance it may be that the change of attitude has been lost between the training centre and the bridge. Positive attitudes can be encouraged, and one reason for the lack of a connection between college classroom and reality could be the lack of a mentoring culture. A major issue on board ships today is that often Masters just do not spend enough time with their junior officers, getting to know them, chatting with them and gradually gaining an understanding of their strengths and weaknesses.

This was particularly evident in the case of the *Paula C*, as mentioned in Section 3, page 37, where an inexperienced third officer was left alone on watch in a highly complex situation. He certainly had not been on board long enough for the Master to evaluate his ability to keep a solo watch in the Dover Strait.

As vessels get ever larger and more complex with continually evolving bridge equipment, safe navigation practices help build a culture of excellence in the bridge team. If junior officers are encouraged to understand the culture of excellence they will continue to apply those principles throughout their careers.

Case study

Hamburg grounding, Sound of Mull, May 2015. There were significant shortcomings in the conduct of navigation on board *Hamburg*, which were compounded by almost non-existent teamwork between the officers on the bridge. While the officers were using ECDIS for navigation, the deck cadet was plotting positions on paper charts. The cadet's chart work was substandard in many respects, but his activities were not being monitored by the OOW. In consequence, useful information about the vessel's position, heading and proximity to dangers was not being assimilated by the bridge team.

Seven minutes before the grounding, both the OOW and the cadet plotted the vessel's position on the chart. Both plotted positions were incorrect, but the cadet's fix did at least indicate that the vessel was running into danger. Unfortunately, he did not feel empowered to challenge the OOW and erased his own position, leaving the OOW's incorrect position on the chart. This action went unremarked because the OOW was not monitoring the cadet's chart work. Proper attention to the cadet's activities would have helped motivate him to perform appropriately and would have empowered him to contribute useful information to the bridge team.

By accepting and approving inadequate passage plans and by not checking that either the ECDIS was being used effectively or that the chart work was to an acceptable standard, the Master was signalling to his officers that he was not concerned about the standards of navigation on board, and they took their lead from him.

The individuals on the bridge were working in isolation, with no recognition of their individual responsibilities and so did not provide the Master with the assistance he required to maintain his situational awareness. During *Hamburg*'s approach to Tobermory there were many opportunities when a suitable challenge from one of the officers might have helped avert the grounding.

Monitoring using VDR

VDR data taken from vessels after accidents have provided evidence of how vessels normally operate away from the scrutiny of company officials. Reluctance to follow procedures and complacent attitudes can be identified and addressed by monitoring the activities of ship staff during random audits of VDR data.

Remote monitoring can reveal:

- How often the under-keel clearance or closest position of approach parameters were contravened
- How many times a helm order produced an angle of list that exceeded the limit set by the company
- The degree to which shipping channels and traffic separation schemes were followed.

Different navigational limits can be set and remotely monitored. Infringement trends can then be analysed and corrective actions and/or additional training can be provided.

Regular analysis of bridge VDR data can supplement navigation assessments to identify navigation errors. VDR data can be useful in informing a full onboard assessment but will not reveal attitudes or work practices on the bridge.

Case study

Maersk Kendal grounding, Singapore Strait, September 2009. The report found that the company's comprehensive guidance and procedures for the vessel were not being followed.

The presence of an internal or external assessor on board will encourage crews to comply with procedures and work routines. This is recognised in a European Union directive, 2009/18/EC, which encourages the use of VDR data for accident investigation and as a preventative tool. The directive advocates the routine examination of VDR data to observe watchkeeping standards under normal operating conditions. In this way, ship managers can understand the elements that could lead to accidents or incidents.

From the Transport Malta Marine Safety Investigation Report no 7/2016 (in Section 3 page 43) safety actions taken by the owners of the *Tongala* included making use of the VDR as a training aid. VDR extracts can be a valuable in assisting the shipboard management team to review navigational practices on board.

Putting training into practice

One correspondent made the following observation about navigation assessments.

66 *Navigation assessments should not be viewed as quality assurance by inspection but as benchmarking and professional mentoring, giving those who need it the opportunity to catch up rather than hide their issues. This is the true value of the navigation assessment.* 99

Attitude on board

Good and bad attitudes on board are related to competency and performance. Complacent individuals behave and think in a predictable mode and don't anticipate any extraordinary developments. We may keep vigilant and alert when we expect matters to develop in complex ways, but can become complacent when everything appears to be going to plan. No one chooses to be complacent; it is a feeling that can affect even normally responsible, sensible mariners, who then find themselves unprepared for situations developing unexpectedly. Complacency weakens the mariner's situational awareness, leading to surprise when the unexpected happens so they react too late or not at all.

NI LinkedIn group

66 *There must be a process in place that identifies gaps and a system that deals with the outcomes. It must be a regular occurrence, so that people understand it is coming and they may as well be prepared and follow the rules. There must be a results review system in place to identify whether it is people or the procedure that is wrong.* 99

Some elements to consider when assessing good attitude:

● Plans are reconsidered if conditions changes or when problems occur
● Assistance is sought if required
● Balanced discussion of options is discussed with relevant team members
● There is evidence of a contingency plan
● People are decisive and make decisions in a timely manner.

Watch out for these as indicative of poor attitude:

● Alternative ideas are never asked for
● Views or opinions of others in the team are ignored
● Aggressive arguments
● Same approach to every situation
● Inability to make decisions under pressure.

Case study

Lysblink Seaways grounding, Kilchoan, February 2015. The report highlighted the disconnection between the owners' procedures and the practices prevalent on board.

The company had a policy of no alcohol on board yet the frequent replenishment of the bonded store was never questioned. The SMS was not followed; there was a poor standard of passage planning; there was no use of lookouts, BNWAS, night orders or emergency checklists; and after the grounding there was a delay in contacting the coastal state. Some of these deficiencies should have been detected by an assessment or audit.

As the assessor becomes more familiar with company requirements they may take on more of a coaching role. The assessment part of the process can be completed fairly quickly. There are almost always quiet times in the voyage (or after arrival in port) when the assessor can spend quality time with the junior officers either collectively or on a one-to-one basis for coaching on the issues observed during the assessment.

Over time, the assessor will be welcomed on board, and ships' officers will see this time as an opportunity to ask questions on matters they have concerns about. The

SMS can be changed by sea staff, as they should own it, although they may never have thought of raising the issues themselves.

One assessor saw a Master who regularly told the bridge team his thoughts before taking action. Rather than being intimidated by the assessor, the Master and officers welcomed the assessment as reinforcement of what they did well. When told about aspects that required improvement, they incorporated the assessor's comments as guidelines for the future.

Assessments are opportunities to explore the gaps in actions, to coach and to mentor the ship's staff. This is a more useful outcome than sheaves of paper full of observations that the Master alone has to deal with.

Section 5

The human element

Assessors should have some understanding of the human element. People manage the whole process of a ship's life from design to operation and from crewing to salvage. Humans devise regulations and surveys, and investigate incidents when things go wrong.

Assessments should observe how the bridge team is performing in terms of human performance. This encompasses how team players work with each other and what their strengths and weaknesses are. Look for evidence of the bridge team concept of working, ensuring that all team members understand their duties.

There should be effective closed-loop communications between bridge team members during manoeuvring and evidence that they are checking each other's actions to avoid single-person error.

The mariner can gain much useful information from the UK MCA's publication *Human Element: a guide to human behaviour in the shipping industry* and The Nautical Institute publication *Human Performance and Limitation for Mariners*.

Case study

Costa Concordia grounding, Giglio, January 2012. There are many lessons to be learned from this incident, but of greatest relevance to the study of the human element is the passive attitude of the bridge team. No one warned the Master of approaching danger. The Master assumed the con when he arrived on the bridge without being adequately aware of the position of the ship and he did not share his intentions and expected outcomes of the decisions he made. This autocratic style of leadership of the Master diminished the chances that his officers would speak up.

So how should we assess aspects of human nature? Here are some principles to consider.

Working with others

Observe the ways in which individuals focused on independent goals work and exchange information with others. For instance, safe watchkeeping is both an independent goal and a team goal. A proper handover to the relieving officer must be provided.

Case study

CMA CGM Florida/Chou Shan collision, East China Sea, March 2013. Communication on the VHF radio was in Mandarin by the Chinese second officer, which left the Filipino OOW to deal with the consequences of conversations he neither understood nor was able to control. The Chinese second officer did not convey fully to the Filipino OOW the content and outcome of his VHF radio communications with *Chou Shan*'s OOW. It was never established whether the two individuals had direct interpersonal conflicts.

Working in teams

If they are to achieve a shared goal, people must work with each other in mutually supportive ways. A bridge team requires people to work with each other as team members, each of whom contributes their effort to an objective that is bigger than any one of them. To promote good teamwork and technical skills, people need social skills that ensure effective interaction between each other.

The assessor needs to recognise individual and team interaction skills, and understand how they are different and what can go wrong.

Case study

Spring Glory/Josephine Mærsk, Singapore Strait, June 2012. This case was mentioned in Section 3 (page 40) with regard to Colregs. Now we can reflect on it to consider the lack of teamwork shown. On both ships the OOW was the third officer and probably the least experienced of the ship's officers without the experience to recognise their human and technical limitations. Although qualified to be responsible for the watch, neither OOW recognised that they needed assistance until it was too late.

The assessor should be wary of their own human limitations when observing the ship's staff and in making notes. In particular, they need to be aware of their own natural biases. For example, if someone is good at a particular task, that aptitude is likely to exert a positive influence on rankings given for other activities – even in the absence of any evidence. Conversely, if they are poor in some activity, the assessor tends to have a negative view of all their activities. This is known as the Halo/Horns effect.

The Mathew Effect is a variation on the Halo/Horns effect and refers to the tendency for people to be judged in the same way they have always been judged.

The assessor should also be aware of Recency Bias, in which the person's most recent performance exerts an undue influence, regardless of how they might have performed earlier.

The temptation is to take the easy option and mark in the middle of the scale when considering the bridge team performance. The scoring system used in the assessment criteria used in Section 6 does not have a middle scale and is aimed at assisting the assessor to make objective judgements.

Another risk is that people could be rated higher than they merit, perhaps because the assessor seeks to avoid confrontation and argument about poor performance.

An assessment could be based on how a person is functioning at a particular moment rather than being based on an overall picture of their performance. This is why it is essential to allow sufficient time for navigation assessments so that the assessor can gain a deeper understanding of each team member's performance and competence.

Communicating with others

In order to communicate effectively with people from different cultures the assessor may need to change the way they normally interact. They need to be aware, for example, that some people may say one thing but their body language conveys a different message entirely.

Questions should be formatted so that people can demonstrate with their answer that they have understood the question. Some people may not be comfortable being interrogated in front of others, so the assessor may need to consider talking to those individuals on a one-to-one basis.

A common language on board the vessel is important to avoid misunderstandings and the assessor should take note of the language spoken on the bridge between ship's staff and between the bridge and the shore.

Case study

Wes Janine/Stenberg collision, Brunsbüttel, January 2014. Communication between the pilot and the shore was conducted in German. The Polish master of the ship was unable to follow this exchange and so did not have sufficient knowledge of the situation. There was no evidence from the VDR that the Master discussed this with the pilot.

Ships' command teams need to be proactive and request pilots to exchange information and conduct conversations in English.

Most crews of merchant ships are multinational and culturally diverse. For the majority of companies this looks likely to remain the case for some time. Multilingual crews must establish a common working language. In most cases this will be English. However, some members of the crew may not possess a good command of the language. Even if they have only restricted language skills, they should be encouraged to use English. Because it is relatively free of hierarchy, the language tends to promote teamwork. This is one of the reasons it was adopted in the aviation industry (where multinational crews are also common), and its use in the cockpit has helped to reduce junior aviation staff members' inhibitions in challenging more senior colleagues.

Multilingual crews are made up of seafarers with very different language standards, which are a barrier to selecting a common language for use on board. Misunderstandings may arise when the same term is translated in different ways according to the original language.

Watchkeeping officers are required to have a standard of written and spoken English that enables them to understand charts, nautical publications, meteorological information and messages concerning the ship's safety and operation. Their knowledge should also be adequate to communicate with other ships and coast stations and multilingual crews and to use IMO standard maritime communication phrases.

Cultural understanding

Intercultural communication is vital for success in the maritime world. Effective communication between colleagues from different cultural backgrounds ensures teams work harmoniously. Empathy is essential for appreciating and understanding people whose cultures differ from one's own.

Understanding comes from individuals having the same interpretation of words or gestures. Having some sort of cultural understanding will help to put communication and behaviour in context.

At the end of the 1970s, psychologist Dr Geert Hofstede published his internationally recognised standard for understanding cultural differences based on a decade of research, *Culture's Consequences* (see Further Reading, page 82). This identifies several ways in which national cultures stand out from each other, all with implications for communications.

Power distance

Understanding about power distance – of how far away the power is from the rest of the team – will help the assessor to evaluate bridge cultures and understand why some officers don't challenge their superiors.

Case study

Conti Peridot/Carla Mærsk collison, Houston Ship Channel, March 2015. The Master and the pilot could not be heard discussing the vessel's navigation leading up to the collision. The Master did not engage, such as by asking the pilot if everything was all right, or suggesting he slow down or call the oncoming ship. Probably this was because he was unaware of the vessel's heading fluctuations and was reluctant to speak up about them. Cultural factors can contribute to such hesitation. The pilot on the *Conti Peridot* stated that, in his experience, certain cultures tended to be more deferential and would not challenge a pilot.

Case study

CMA CGM Florida/Chou Shan collision, East China Sea, March 2013. Current research suggests that, culturally, the Chinese second officer, although of equivalent rank to the Filipino second officer, is likely to have been respectful of the Filipino second officer's age, experience and authority as the OOW.

Case study

Bow Mariner explosion off the coast of Virginia, February 2004. The culture prevalent on board followed the Hofstede model. The Master, chief officer and chief engineer were Greek and the other officers and crew were Filipinos. The distinctions between the nationalities were significant. Filipino officers did not take their meals in the officers' mess, were given almost no responsibility and were closely supervised in every task.

This lack of trust meant the chief officer would not sleep, beyond short naps, during cargo operations. He performed all management and administrative duties himself, did not delegate or attempt to train the junior officers, either to reduce his own workload or provide for their professional growth. The Filipino officers had little knowledge of the technical aspects of their job. As a result, they failed to question unsafe actions or procedures.

Case study

Bunga Teratai Satu grounding, Great Barrier Reef, November 2000. The senior officers were from Pakistan and the ratings from Malaysia; there was a strict hierarchy between them. Before the grounding, the mate was engaged in making telephone calls on his mobile phone. The AB plotted the vessel position on the chart but was not familiar with charts and navigation and did not realise the ship was standing into danger. He resumed his lookout duties assuming the mate would check the position and did not feel it was his place to suggest to the mate he should alter course. This strict hierarchy was seen as normal, but this kind of working environment increases the likelihood of single-person error.

Risk taking

The assessor needs to have a good understanding of risk management and control measures so the assessment identifies key hazards. They should assess the effectiveness of control measures such as:

- Physical equipment, including radars and ECDIS
- Administrative procedures and checklists
- Supervisory elements – is the Master guiding the junior officers?

Perceived value

The more a course of action appears to support a goal that crew members regard as important or highly desirable, the less risky it will appear to be to them. They are more likely to overlook the risks normally associated with that task.

Perceived familiarity

The more familiar circumstances or tasks seem, the less risky they will appear to be. Complacency is often mentioned in the shipping industry. It sets in when people allow familiarity to blunt their sensitivity to risk.

Based on their experience, the assessor should be able to evaluate levels of perceived familiarity and complacency. Officers doing routine and repeated tasks are in danger of becoming complacent. For instance, it could be that senior officers have worked for companies for so long and are so familiar with the SMS and circular letters that they no longer look at them.

The attitude of the assessor and their handling of the different elements making up the bridge team (including multiculturalism) help ensure a much more comprehensive assessment of navigation practices.

Section 6

Navigation assessments criteria

This list of criteria is available as a PDF for download at
www.nautinst.org/navigationassessments

Scoring

Scoring scale
4 = best practice
3 = acceptable
2 = needs improvement
1 = unacceptable;
NA = not applicable

ASSESSMENT AREA	SCORE	COMMENTS
Passage plan – Stage 1 – Preliminary		
Passage Plan – Stage 2 – Appraisal and risk assessment		
Passage Plan – Stage 3 – Planning		
Bridge team briefing on passage plan		
Passage plan – monitoring of passage		
Alternative passage plan		
No-go areas/abort points discussed and plotted		
Equipment tested/status verified		

Navigation assessments – a guide to best practice

Bridge team organisation – manning levels		
Effective use of bridge equipment		
Monitoring instruments		
Traffic appreciation		
Application of Colregs		
Track management		
Communication management		
Anticipation/decision-making		
Situational awareness		
Bridge team management		
Response to stress		
Delegation of duties		
Confidence		
Pilotage – overall		
Discussion with pilot including amendments to passage plan and mooring or tug arrangements		
Integration of pilot		
Monitoring of pilot		
Master's standing/night orders		
Relevant ship handling		
Overall navigation safety		
Watch handover procedure		
Familiarity with ECDIS		
Cyber-security/hygiene		

Navigation instructions/procedures/ checklists/documents on bridge		
Standard publications available		
Entries in logbooks		
Transfer of con		
Fatigue management (hours of work and rest)		
Compass errors		
Management of navigation warnings		
Familiarity with emergency/ contingency plans		
Control of night vision		
End-of-voyage briefing		
Training		
Maintaining anchor watch		
GMDSS equipment		
Security awareness		
Mentoring		
TOTAL SCORE		
Maximum score		
Overall score (%)		

Navigation assessments – a guide to best practice

Sample scoring

4 = best practice
3 = acceptable
2 = needs improvement
1 = unacceptable
NA = not applicable

ASSESSMENT AREA	SCORE	COMMENTS
Passage plan – Stage 1 – Preliminary	NA	
Passage plan – Stage 2 – Appraisal and risk assessment	3	Limited destination port information
Passage plan – Stage 3 – Planning	4	Very good plan – well marked up
Bridge team briefing on passage plan	3	Limited time for briefing due to cargo operations
Passage plan – monitoring of passage	3	Parallel indexing not used
Alternative passage plan	NA	
No-go areas/abort points discussed and plotted	4	No-go areas plotted well, abort points marked for critical points
Equipment tested/status verified	4	Using checklists
Bridge team organisation – manning levels	4	Manned appropriately at all times
Effective use of bridge equipment	3	Not using echo sounder to check against charted depths
Monitoring instruments	3	Not always checked when taking over the watch
Traffic appreciation	4	Good overall awareness
Application of Colregs	3	Alteration of course to avoid collision could be more substantial to ensure action is obvious
Track management	4	Allowance for set and drift well planned
Communication management	3	Limitations in using English when communicating with shore stations

Anticipation/decision-making	4	Helped by well marked-up passage plan
Situational awareness	4	
Bridge team management	4	All aware of their roles
Response to stress	NA	
Delegation of duties	4	
Confidence	3	
Pilotage – overall	4	
Discussion with pilot including amendments to passage plan and mooring/tug arrangements	4	Positive and thorough to update passage plan
Integration of pilot	4	Welcoming
Monitoring of pilot	4	Good checking with pilot on his intentions
Master's standing/night orders	4	Well-written, covered relevant points
Relevant ship handling	NA	
Overall navigation safety	4	All key elements covered
Watch handover procedure	3	Not always recorded in logbook
Familiarity with ECDIS	3	Some non-critical functions not familiar
Cyber-security/hygiene	1	Mobile phone charged using ECDIS USB port; officers not aware of cyber hygiene issues
Navigation instructions/procedures/checklists/documents on bridge	3	Less than full understanding of risks with checked items on checklists
Standard publications available	4	
Entries in logbooks	2	Few entries for weather experienced; watch handover; transfer of con
Transfer of con	2	Frequently not observed audibly
Fatigue management (hours of work and rest)	4	Well-managed, anticipated where extra manning required and work schedule amended to accommodate
Compass errors	2	Only compared pre-departure

Navigation assessments – a guide to best practice

Management of navigation warnings	4	
Familiarity with emergency/contingency plans	4	All aware of plans and conducted GNSS failure drill
Control of night vision	4	
End-of-voyage briefing	3	Full debrief not carried out due to cargo operations commencing immediately
Training	4	All aware of training opportunities offered
Maintaining anchor watch	NA	
GMDSS equipment	4	Watchkeeping and log entries only
Security awareness	NA	
Mentoring	1	No mentoring observed
TOTAL SCORE	**136**	
Maximum score	**160**	
Overall score (%)	**85**	

Annex I

A maritime skills gap, fact or fiction?

Concern within the industry is reflected in this document

Author: The Standard Club
Contact details: +65 6506 2852 or yves.vandenborn@ctplc.com

Introduction

Serious navigation-related accidents are unfortunately common in the maritime industry, despite a revolution in bridge technology. Considering the resources expended by the industry to comply with the ISM Code and to recruit properly qualified officers, the question remains whether there is a significant gap between the aims of STCW/ISM and the reality on board many ships.

The statistics

The European Maritime Safety Agency's (EMSA) annual overview of marine incidents and casualties 2015 showed a rise in the reported number of maritime casualties and incidents from 1,271 in 2011 to 3,025 in 2014. During this period, navigation-based incidents accounted for 34% of all incidents recorded by EMSA. Most of these incidents would have occurred on board a vessel with a certified safety management system (SMS) and manned by officers trained to at least STCW standard. Such findings are comparable to the club's claims data, which has recorded an increasing trend of collision, fixed and floating object and grounding claims between the years 2013 and 2015. On average, 420 such incidents have been recorded each year. Many of these claims were attributable to basic failures in watchkeeping, failure to follow agreed passage planning, failure to confirm the operational status of navigation equipment or poor application of the collision regulations.

Annex 1
Navigation assessments – a guide to best practice

The Standard Club's response

In response to this concern, The Standard Club has developed its own Navigation Risk Assessment process, which involves passive observation of watchkeepers during their normal bridge activities.

This was the club's response to the evidence that basic requirements of safe navigation and watchkeeping were not being maintained on board some ships. It is the club's view that the close observation of a crew in an operational setting enables a third party to determine the true standard of navigation being practised on a daily basis. Such observation enables the assessor to gauge what standards of navigation each deck officer believes is appropriate for safe watchkeeping. It also reveals their attitude to the SMS and whether they engage in behaviours likely to contribute to a hazardous incident.

Behaviours have been witnessed frequently by the club's surveyors when conducting these Navigation Risk Assessments that are a cause for concern. Deck officers have been observed engaging in low level SMS non-compliance and more serious hazardous behaviours right up to command level. When such behaviour has been observed in junior deck officers, it has frequently occurred with the tacit approval of senior deck officers who were present on the bridge at the time of the event. The types of non-compliance and hazardous behaviours witnessed from all ranks of deck officers included:

- Failure to conduct effective master-pilot exchanges
- Dangerous over-reliance on electronic navigation aids, such as ECDIS
- Inadequate manning levels on the bridge, particularly at critical periods such as pilot boarding/disembarkation or the final stages of a berthing operation
- Failure to conduct routine compass checks over extended periods
- Failure to maintain a proper lookout by all available means

The key issues

We consider the attitude of masters toward the enforcement of SMS procedures as the main cause of a poor safety culture. Masters must be the drivers of high safety standards on board their ships and should rigorously enforce SMS compliance. This enforcement should include the smaller, less critical requirements of watchkeeping (such as gyro compass checks) and the high-risk areas such as safe manning levels and master-pilot exchanges. Masters must lead by example and promote both the requirements and benefits of ISM. Officers should comply, because they recognise its obvious benefits in terms of safety for themselves, their colleagues and the ship and not because they are forced by threat of sanction.

Summary

Companies should be aware that the possession of a certificate of competency (CoC) alone may not guarantee quality in terms of performance. It is also valuable for companies to examine their accident/near miss reports for trends of non-compliance or poor safety culture. With question marks being raised over the effectiveness of ISM and CoC for maintaining standards of navigation, The Standard Club foresees the Navigation Risk Assessment becoming an essential tool for the upkeep of navigation standards in the future.

66 *Quality means doing it right when no one is looking* 99 **(Henry Ford)**

Further reading

Navigation Accidents and their Causes
(The Nautical Institute, 2015, ISBN 978 1 906915 32 2)

Human Performance and Limitation for Mariners
(The Nautical Institute, 2015, ISBN 978 1 906915 34 6)

Mentoring at Sea – the 10 minute challenge
(The Nautical Institute, 2012, ISBN 978 1 906915 48 3)

Code of Safe Working Practices for Merchant Seafarers
(TSO, 2015, ISBN 978 0 11553402 7; also available as PDF from https://www.gov.uk/government/publications/code-of-safe-working-practices-for-merchant-seafarers)

Culture's Consequences: Comparing Values, Behaviors, Institutions, and Organisations Across Nations
(2nd edition, Sage Publications, 2003, ISBN 978 0 80397324 4)

Guidelines for the recording of events relating to navigation
(IMO, MSC Circ.A916 (22))

The Guidelines on Cyber Security Onboard Ships
(BIMCO, CLIA, ICS, Intercargo and Intertanko, 2016, https://www.bimco.org/News/2016/01/04_Cyber_security_guidelines.aspx)

The human element: a guide to human behaviour in the shipping industry
(TSO, 2010, ISBN 978 0 11553120 0; also available as PDF from https://www.gov.uk/government/uploads/system/uploads/attachment_data/file/283000/the_human_element_a_guide_to_human_behaviour_in_the_shipping_industry.pdf)

The Human Element
(MGN520, Maritime & Coastguard Agency, forthcoming – available November 2017)

ICS Bridge Procedure Guide (BPG5)
(http://www.ics-shipping.org/docs/default-source/publications-for-homepage/ics-bridge-procedures-guide-order-form-2016.pdf?sfvrsn=16)

IMO Standard Marine Communication Phrases
(IMO, 2002, ISBN 978 92 801 4211 2; available from The Nautical Institute)

Industry Guidelines for ECDIS Familiarisation
(The Nautical Institute, 2012, http://www.nautinst.org/filemanager/root/site_assets/forums/ecdis_forum/ecdis-full_document-b.pdf)

International Convention for the Safety of Life at Sea 1974 (as amended), Chapter V – Safety of Navigation
(SOLAS Consolidated Edition, IMO, 2014, ISBN 978 92 801 1594 9; available from The Nautical Institute)

The Mariner's Handbook
(10th edition, NP100, UK Hydrographic Office, 2015, ISBN 978 0 70774163 5)

The Standard Club Safety Bulletin June 2012
(http://www.standard-club.com/media/23772/17054StandardSafetyNavigation-2012.pdf)

About the author

Captain Harry Gale FNI

Harry Gale began his seagoing career as a cadet with Trident Tankers Ltd (part of the P&O Group) in 1967 and obtained his Master's Foreign Going certificate in 1977. After working on board bulk, general cargo and container vessels with various companies, he worked ashore with the Hydrographic Office and the Met Office before joining The Nautical Institute as Technical Manager in 2007.

He has a key role in progressing the influential work of the Institute, involving research on professional and technical issues within the industry. He represents the Institute at IMO, on committees and at conferences.

He obtained a BSc (Hons) degree with the Open University in 2004 and is a Fellow of The Nautical Institute.

Captain Gale is author of the Institute's book *From Paper Charts to ECDIS: A Practical Voyage Plan*, which is now in its second edition.